Dark Matter Monsters:
Cryptids, Ball Lightning, and the Science of Secret Lifeforms

by Simeon Hein, Ph.D.

Cover by Mark Tuchman

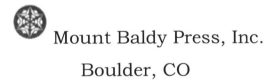

Mount Baldy Press, Inc.

Boulder, CO

Dark Matter Monsters: Cryptids, Ball Lightning, and the Science of Secret Lifeforms

Mount Baldy Press, Inc.
PO Box 469
Boulder, CO 80306
415-413-8052

MountBaldy.com

1st Edition, July 2022

2nd Edition, August 2022

Cover by Mark Tuchman

Printed in the United States of America

Publisher's Cataloging-in-Publication data

Names: Hein, Simeon, author.
Title: Dark matter monsters : cryptids , ball lightning , and the science of secret lifeforms / by Simeon Hein, Ph.D
Description: Includes bibliographical references and index. | Boulder, CO: Mount Baldy Press, Inc., 2022.
Identifiers: LCCN: 2022938094 | ISBN: 978-0-9715863-9-0 (paperback) | 978-0-9715863-8-3 (Kindle)
Subjects: LCSH Parapsychology and science. | Human-alien encounters. | Monsters. | Unidentified flying objects. | Curiosities and wonders. | Physics--Philosophy. | Science--Philosophy. | BISAC BODY, MIND & SPIRIT / Unexplained Phenomena | SCIENCE / Physics / Electromagnetism | SOCIAL SCIENCE / General
Classification: LCC BF1045.S33 .H45 2022 | DDC 130--dc23

Table of Contents

Dedication

This book is dedicated to Claire from the UK, who encountered unknown creatures near Carmel Highlands and the Sea Otter Reserve, CA, in 1989 and was told to keep quiet and threatened by responding law enforcement officers. And to all the other witnesses to these mysterious lifeforms and phenomena.

Acknowledgements

This book would not have been possible without the contributions of so many brave people who shared their stories with me. It's been a genuinely fractal experience, as the more people I mentioned the book-in-progress to, the more folks shared their bigfoot stories with me. So thanks to Nia, Lauren, Bob, Barb, Dan, Randy, Jules, Teri and Randy, Robert, Mike and Leah, Dan, Lynn, Genise and Bruce, Lucy, and many others with whom I've talked over the years at events and conferences. Thanks to researchers like Jim Myers at the Sasquatch Outpost, Don Monroe, Harriet McFeely, Igor Burtsev, Matt Heines, and Ron Morehead. Colin Andrews helped me with specific details of the Ray Barnes crop circle incident. Ron Russell refreshed my memory on some of his strange, magnetic crop circle experiences. And thanks to Project Hessdalen for the use of their photos. Kudos to open-minded podcasters Wes Germer of Sasquatch Chronicles, Dave Scott of Spaced Out Radio, Andy McGrillen, Dan Zetterstrom of That UFO Podcast, and many others. John Hauser for challenging discussions about the applications of mathematics at The Laughing Goat. And none of this would have happened without the tremendous work of Robert William Greenyer and the non-profit Martin Fleischmann Memorial Project. Shera was super helpful with her comments on an early version of this book. Terry Lovelace gave helpful feedback and ideas. And to all the cryptids and dark matter monsters out there, I appreciate your ideas, howls, luminosities, and inspiring vibes. Susan and

Pretzel listened to all my ramblings about this topic for months. Any errors or mistakes in the following book are my responsibility and not those of anyone listed above.

And special thanks to graphics artists who make their work available online through the public domain to creators like myself. Artist Mark Tuchman did a fantastic job converting my thoughts into a great cover. Thanks also to Ira G. Liss and Eva Giddings for their artistic contributions.

Table of Figures

Warning: Bigfoot and other cryptids can behave unpredictably and create unknown or damaging biophysical effects on people and pets. These effects can include battery and camera failure, memory lapses, confusion, and time loss. While bigfoot, in particular, have been known to be helpful to people and children, even rescuing them from dangerous situations, the opposite outcome can also happen leading to long-term mental anxiety, PTSD, serious injury or death. Please keep your distance from these creatures, if possible, unless you're in the presence of an experienced guide or professional researcher.

Preface

When I was a young child, my mom would read me the book *Where the Wild Things Are* by Maurice Sendak, a fictional children's story about an island of wild creatures. I knew even back then that this was a fictional account, and even though there was a scary element to the storyline, it was just a story. And as we all grew older, we were told that such stories are just fantasy and entertainment for young children.

There's only one problem. That's wrong: monsters really do exist and in many varieties. I'm not talking about your typical movie science fiction monsters like *Frankenstein* of old or Marvel Comics movies that you see on the big screen.

The real "monsters" out there have been witnessed by tens or even hundreds of thousands of people in forests, remote landscapes, beaches, next to houses, and on the edge of rural shopping malls. They appear to be flesh and blood entities with a solid appearance, sometimes leave giant footprints, break branches, can howl or scream like there's no tomorrow, or push down huge trees.

Yet, they also have other properties that don't fit within a flesh and blood description, making them seem "paranormal" for lack of a better word. They can seemingly become invisible, generate luminosity, talk telepathically to your mind, warp your sense of time, and teleport to other locations. Yes, these behaviors have all been reported by witnesses and more.

Are they really and truly monsters? Not in my view (though I could be wrong): They are most likely lifeforms based on non-ordinary states of matter that science has yet to fully recognize; perhaps because they have different fundamental characteristics than we're used to. They may even be an ancient precursor or relative of modern humans.

For example, many witnesses have reported seeing a bigfoot or Sasquatch creature in front them one moment and then vanishing in thin air the next. Or even more bafflingly, transforming into an object like a tree branch or trunk or even a boulder. They seem to "glide" around trees, over trails, or move through dense, thick forest at rapid speeds that would have us tripping over and falling down. Their tracks seemingly disappear in the middle of trackable ground. As Navajo Ranger Jonathan Dover, an experienced law enforcement professional, put it on the *Podcast UFO with Martin Willis*, "it's like something just picked them up into space, or they disappeared into another dimension." [1]

We've been taught that we are the most advanced species on the planet, and most of us believe that idea to the core. Humans are the biological pinnacle of nature's creation, right? The "Apex Predator." But let's say it isn't true? What if a previous human-related species had abilities that we've lost over time: They are still around and very good at staying concealed when they want to be?

Sounds implausible on the surface, but the empirical evidence overwhelmingly points to something like this scenario. Witnesses to bigfoot and other cryptids report hearing telepathic voices in their heads just before an encounter, even in their homes, or feeling something invisible has crossed their hiking path close to them. Or is perfectly, invisibly pacing them on a trail or parallel to them in the woods. Personally, after reading and listening to these accounts from hundreds of seemingly sane, ordinary witnesses, I believe them.

Is such a situation possible? Can so many people be having encounters with unidentified lifeforms?

Encounters we haven't been told about in school, by the media, or scientists?

When I wrote my third book, *Black Swan Ghosts* (2017), I interviewed many witnesses to UFO events and ETs, possibly, in some cases. I learned to tell how truthful a story was from the tone of the witnesses' voices, their body language, and general demeanor. Now about ten years later I've listened to bigfoot witnesses, perhaps hundreds of them at this point. And I believe the vast majority of these people are telling the truth. They may not know what they saw, but they know they saw *something* out of the ordinary.

And suppose hundreds, thousands of witnesses have encountered cryptid creatures. In that case, it means our reality is *very different* from what we thought it was. It's a serious situation because people are encountering these creatures and have no idea what to do and where to report their encounter afterwards. For law enforcement, it's just a case of "unidentified wildlife" even if it's bipedal and resembles a human. This can create PTSD (Post Traumatic Stress Syndrome) in witnesses or the law enforcement personnel responding to these human/creature encounter situations, often with dire outcomes. They can suffer mental breakdown afterwards. And then they're unlikely to tell anyone about it, ever again. Consequently, we don't make any progress in understanding or dealing with these types of lifeforms. It's just easier to pretend it "never happened." As one bigfoot witness said: "My experience happened all the way back when I was 19. I'm now 49 . . . It's something that I've avoided mentioning to almost everyone I've ever known." [2]

The following information in this book suggests something important: We are surrounded by and are interacting, from time to time, with biological entities of an entirely different structure and physiological makeup than we're used to. These interactions are heavily underreported because of witnesses' fears of being ridiculed, shamed, and ostracized by their neighbors, friends, and colleagues. This is not unlike military UFO encounters. Therefore, witnesses to these weird phenomena don't say anything about what they've experienced. As a result, our collective understanding of reality is highly distorted and biased towards ordinary phenomena rather than anomalous experiences reported by pilots, law enforcement officers, park rangers, and those who enjoy exploring the outdoors. In short, we have almost no idea what's going on out there. And the stranger the encounter, the more likely that none of us will ever hear about it. It's like a self-effacing negative feedback loop of ignorance and denial.

Jacques Vallée pointed out a similar situation concerning UFO witnesses: "the stranger the encounters, the less likely they are to share their experience." And that situation creates a huge gap in our understanding of reality.

Introduction

"Surely the true path is to dive deep into nature."
—Vincent Van Gogh

It all started for me in 2017 when a friend gave me some "bigfoot socks": socks with a bigfoot image sown into the sides of them, that she had purchased at a bigfoot museum in Bailey, Colorado. She said I should visit it someday; I'd like it. Bigfoot museum? At the time, bigfoot for me was some type of mythical creature or undiscovered primate, as cryptozoologist Loren

Fig. 1. The Bigfoot Socks that
Started my Adventure
(Photo by Author)

Coleman had said back on *The Art Bell Show* sometime in the late 90s.

Coleman estimated there were about 1,500 or so of these creatures in the North-West US and they were most likely an ancient, undiscovered type of ape or anthropoid. He gave many examples of animals that weren't believed in when they were initially first seen, such as giant squid (first described as sea serpents) or Mountain   Gorillas   in   Africa. His

Fig. 2. Frame 352 Showing "Patty" from
Patterson-Gimlin Film, 1967

perspective seemed plausible, and I never gave it much thought afterward. Yes, I had seen the famous Patterson-Gimlin footage of "Patty" as a movie preview as a teenager in the late 1970s. But the topic just wasn't on my radar. Maybe the Patterson-Gimlin footage creature was just a guy in a monkey suit? I didn't necessarily believe this, but I couldn't discount the possibility either. Many decades later it seems increasingly unlikely that Patty was a hoax. No one has been able to disprove or recreate it. Many "Pattys" have been seen since then, and there's no evidence that humans can walk like that, making huge strides, arms dangling down to their knees with legs as big as tree trunks.

In Fall 2019, a friend and I were traveling back from Sedona, AZ, and just happened to stop for gas in Bailey, Colorado, on route 285. I saw a side road I had never been on before and suggested we drive down to exit town. And there it was: "The Sasquatch Outpost." It was still open that day, and we went in.

This wasn't a small, dusty museum by any means:

Fig. 3. The Sasquatch Outpost—Bailey, Colorado
(Photo by Author)

there were a lot of displays, plaster casts of footprints, possible hair samples, and lots of photos of braided horse manes, strange tree structures, and a huge, towering lifelike Bigfoot statue (which has now been replaced by an even more lifelike "screaming" model). And there was a map of the entire Colorado Front Range portion of the Rocky Mountains: colored dots had been placed to mark where howling sounds, tree knockings, tree structures, footprints, and direct sightings had been mapped out. And these little dots on the map were not all that far from Boulder, Colorado, my hometown. Some of the dots were just at the edge of town.

Fig. 4. One of the Bigfoot Encounter Maps Created by The Sasquatch Outpost (Photo by Author)

Suddenly, right then and there, the subject became real to me. Some of these sightings or encounters were only a few miles from where I lived at the time. And from that point on, I started to read different books on the subject. There were books of encounters by Rusty Wilson from places like Yellowstone and Glacier National Parks, Tom Lyons from various locations throughout North America, and many others. I had been on some of the trails where these encounters allegedly happened, so the stories hit home. I even wrote a finger-picking tune around one of these trails in Glacier called "Avalanche Creek" and put it on an album of guitar instrumentals (*Night on Mt. Graham*, 1985).

Hidden Events

Around the same time, someone contacted me with a similar last name to mine. He had also graduated from WSU in Pullman, WA: Matthew Heines of the appropriately titled podcast "Encounters USA." I went on the show, and Matt asked me about crop circles and remote viewing.[3] He then asked what I thought about bigfoot and something called "dogman." Really? Dogman? Was Matt kidding me or something? I realized I didn't know enough to answer his questions. So I started reading about all these topics.

And the more I read, the more I realized that this was what sociologists call a "Hidden Event," just like I had written about in *Black Swan Ghosts*. The idea was studied by sociologist Dr. Ron Westrum of Eastern Michigan University. A Hidden Event is something that many people experience but won't talk about because of fear of ridicule or ostracism or because society says it isn't real. It used to refer to child abuse that wasn't recognized or given attention in the United States until the mid-1960s. It seems to take a focused effort by experts, institutions, and professionals to finally agree that something is real before society as a whole can talk about it.

The more I dug into the topic of bigfoot and cryptids, the more witnesses I encountered: witnesses who were often reluctant to share their stories.

Then I started watching and listening to YouTube Bigfoot shows: *Survivorman Bigfoot*, *Sasquatch Chronicles*, *Strange Familiars*, *Crypto PTSD*, *Spaced Out Radio*, *ThinkThunker* and others. The quality of these interviews was often excellent with previously unknown encounters and witnesses (at least to me). *Sasquatch Chronicles* alone had passed 800 episodes! I soon realized that perhaps thousands and thousands of people in the US had encountered these creatures or something similar.

But there was something else, something quite extraordinary: Witnesses also reported balls of light, missing time, watches stopping, and other odd phenomena around the bigfoot creatures. What? Balls of light? Orbs? UFOs? Around an undiscovered ape species? What exactly was going on here?

Our Limiting Educational Experiences

If you're like me, you had the typical Western education that taught you what was real, what was fiction, and what was just fantasy. And you went about your life thinking you knew how things worked, the basic structure of reality, and you read many books and magazines, and newspapers supporting those views. And just about everyone else you knew did the same. It's the practical, modern way to go.

There's only one problem: the version of reality that you and I were taught, the modern viewpoint, is simply wrong. *It's a delusion.* Because well below the stream of news, facts, and information we receive every day from the mainstream media is another world: the world of Hidden Events. It didn't take long for me to realize that this term described peoples' encounters with these cryptid creatures. And people who have experienced Hidden Events can risk going into a "social danger zone" where they could be ostracized and ridiculed by their peers.

All sorts of bad things can happen to you in a social danger zone. You could lose your professional reputation and be threatened by your colleagues as a nut case. You could lose your job. You might be subject to a psychological exam that could impact your "personal fitness report" if you work for a commercial airline or serve in the military.

Yet, Hidden Events eventually go mainstream, and witnesses start coming out of the closet, talking to journalists, and giving interviews.

And that same process now is happening with the subject of UFOs, also now called UAPs. The acronym stands for Unidentified Aerial Phenomena or Unidentified Aerospace Phenomena for objects that can transverse space, the atmosphere, and the oceans in ways we don't yet understand. And calling them UAPs instead of UFOs seems less threatening to our collective psyche.

But it goes a lot deeper than that. Because for centuries, even millennia, people have been experiencing strange creatures in the woods and backyards. On camping trips and day hikes. And even at the edge of suburban shopping mall parking lots. Near nuclear plants. And around UFO sightings. These creatures have the popular name "cryptids" because they are creatures that modern science does not yet accept. (Crypt meaning "vault or chamber underground.") Yet there are thousands and thousands of sightings of these creatures in the US alone, by people from all walks of life, policemen, law enforcement personal, people walking their dogs at night or stopping at truck stops or forest service picnic grounds.

Bigfoot, or Sasquatch, Sásqu'ets, Yowie, Grassman, and Bakwas, as some Native Americans referred to them, actually there are hundreds or thousands of names for this creature, has been seen in every state in the United States seemingly going back for decades and centuries. In Russia, it's called an Almasty. In China, Yeren or the Wild Man. Is it an undiscovered ape, a primordial human, an alien being? There's no consensus so far and no official discussion of the subject with some small exceptions (allegedly, some of the US National Forest offices, like Mount Hood in Oregon, have internal bigfoot reporting forms). The higher you go up in the educational and media food chain the more ridicule and scorn, the subject receives even calling the whole thing folklore or an urban legend, as social scientists or psychologists are apt to do. Yet the reports keep coming in, some suggesting violent altercations with these creatures where humans are injured or worse. True, these stories are anecdotal but so were reports of child abuse until the subject was taken seriously in early the 1960s.

We can safely say that the bigfoot encounters are still a Hidden Event around the globe because it's a subject that's seldom discussed in public. You'll find bigfoot conferences here and there with credible witnesses and good presentations of evidence. Yet I've never seen the subject mentioned in *Science Magazine* or *New Scientist* both of which I've been reading for 30 years or so. So what does it take to get this subject out in the open? There are plenty of authors who devote themselves to bringing these stories to the public such as Rusty Wilson, PD King, Ron Morehead, Tom Lyons, Becky Cook, Richard Hunt, Carter Buschardt (just to mention a few) who have published hundreds of encounters reported to them by the public.

Author, UFO experiencer, and former federal prosecutor Terry Lovelace did a similar thing with his book *Devil's Den: The Reckoning* (2020). He collected 30 of the best stories from those sent to him by readers of his first book, *Incident at Devil's Den: A True Story* (2018). I've read through these accounts. Like many others I am left wondering what in the world is going on out there and why do we hear so little about these types of experiences, often from groups of witnesses all reporting similar details from a collective contact event?

For example, Terry received the following story, which I'll summarize. A group of firefighters in Texas decided to go pig hunting on land that one of them owned. After getting to the location and roasting a wild pig they had caught, they saw lights in the nearby trees. Thinking it was another group of hunters, the landowner let off a few shots with his 45 semiautomatic handgun to scare them off. But the lights got brighter. The next thing they know, they can't find one member of their group who had gone in the trailer a few minutes before to rest. Then they all wake up hours later in the early hours of the morning, unable to account for hours of missing time or why that hadn't been able to find their friend, who was now back with them. The campfire had long burned down to ash. One of them started to have nightmares about the incident. They didn't talk about what they had experienced that night for a while afterwords. Finally, they met in a restaurant that one of them owned, and then never again. It was just unexplainable and uncomfortable.

Well, guess what? This type of scenario has been repeated countless times not only with UFO experiences, as chronicled by authors like Preston Dennett, but with cryptid witnesses. The witnesses never want to talk about it again, at least not to their circle of friends and family. They just want to forget the whole thing. But they can't, and they still feel a sense of terror years later especially when alone in nature. No more camping, hiking, or hunting trips. They're done with the great outdoors for good. Here's a typical witness comment: "I can't imagine myself living in the woods or anywhere near them, ever again."[4]

Primordial Particles

I'm writing this book because new discoveries in science reveal another world, another universe, that cohabits in the same space we live in yet is primarily invisible. In my earlier books, like *Black Swan Ghosts*, and *Opening Minds*, I mentioned ideas about the multiverse and people like physicist Hugh Everett III who invented such new interpretations of quantum mechanics. What motivated them to search for new ways to understand our universe. Yet now we have recent evidence from Russian and Japanese scientists about the importance of the Cosmic Background Radiation left over from the Big Bang 13.6 billion years ago. And it all points to the existence of an ancient energetic particle, the "Relic Neutrino," as something essential to life on Earth. Relic neutrinos are primordial particles that continually interact with us and have wavelengths big enough to affect our biological and energetic processes and everything on Earth. And they also promote nuclear transmutation and alchemy, as it were.

According to some scientists, processes like Low Energy Nuclear Reaction (LENR), which used to be called Cold Fusion, thrive on interactions with these cosmic relic neutrinos. So much so that the strength of these processes depends on the time of year. Cold fusion reactions also generate a similar type of particle, called a "cold neutrino." Cold neutrinos and relic neutrinos are the same wavelength and energy but originate from different sources, either the cosmos or terrestrial fusion reactions. They're both equally interactive with chemical and biological activity. These types of "active" neutrinos, neutral particles with a tiny mass, are everywhere in our universe. When they group together in bunches or clusters, weird things happen.

Scientists suspect that relic neutrinos could be the source of dark matter that now makes up roughly 34 percent of the known universe. Another 68 percent is dark energy: the force that pushes galaxies apart at ever-expanding rates. Dark matter interacts with us gravitationally, and that's it. So we can't see it, but we can detect it from the way galaxies spiral around. There's not enough visible mass in any galaxy to account for their rotational speed and gravitational effects. Galactic dark matter might explain that anomaly.

Dark Realities in Our Midst

But what if dark matter were here on Earth, right next to us? Wouldn't it make sense that the animals and creatures here would have found a way to adapt it to their lives in some way? Would they have anomalous traits like invisibility, the ability to morph into other forms, and generate unique types of energy? So if you're willing to take a ride to how this all leads to the existence of cryptic creatures and invisible life, let's take a look.

First off, I'm not a bigfoot researcher. This book is not a comprehensive presentation of all the evidence reported about bigfoot, dogman, thunderbirds, gargoyles, rakes, slide-rock bolters, and other cryptids reputed to be out there. Instead, I aim to summarize the evidence I've collected about these subjects and show how they can fit into a comprehensive physics perspective. I'd also like to show why many of these cryptid encounters are accompanied by "paranormal phenomena" like orbs, light balls, time distortion, creatures' glowing red eyes, gliding motions, levitation, teleportation, telepathy, strange sulphuric smells, battery and camera failure.

In reading the literature and attending many conferences about such topics it became apparent that the same strange phenomena are repeatedly suggesting that there are fundamental scientific principles are at work here. I'm going to accept from the get-go that these creatures exist and have been witnessed by thousands of people and reported by some of them.

Personally, I don't think I've ever directly and knowingly encountered bigfoot, dogman, or any other cryptid to my knowledge, at least physically. However, the overwhelming mass of witness reports from modern and not-so-modern times, Native American stories, and other indigenous peoples are extremely consistent. Even the Vikings reported tall, shrieking bigfoot-type creatures in North America. [5] (Paulides, 2017). There are hundreds and hundreds of recent witnesses, and many have never come forward to tell their tales. They could be your neighbors, colleagues, and relatives. *It seems everyone is describing the same thing, in modern times or long ago.*

I argue here that the types of experiences I've had around crop circles, including strange effects on electronics, and what people report happening to them around bigfoot and other creatures are, in fact, similar phenomena. All of us who are privy to these experiences have encountered COHERENT MATTER PHENOMENA. It follows that the ball lightning people see around thunderstorms, cold fusion devices, UFOs, bigfoot, and crop circles are all the same thing. Yes, I know that's a big claim. Still, science progresses through careful and intelligent simplification, not multiplying entities endlessly and creating new types of explanations with each piece of new evidence, year after year. I believe much of what people call "paranormal phenomena" fundamental and basic processes of science consistent throughout our known universe. It works the same way on Earth as it would a planet in another part of our galaxy. Matter behaves the same way everywhere, as far as we know, at least in our universe. And that means when it undergoes what scientists call a "phase transition," you're going to get the same thing here as anywhere else. Lifeforms that were here long before we were may have adapted to condensed matter properties and used them to their advantage. This includes cloaking, superfluidity, antigravity, and other exotic properties.

Researchers in cold fusion experiments, such as Takaaki Matsumoto and Alexander Parkhomov, have reported strange phenomena around their experiments bordering on the paranormal. These include balls of light, gravity decay, EMF pulses, and anomalous radiation. I'm arguing here in this book that these are the same phenomena we see around purportedly haunted sights, cryptids, and UFOs. These are all varieties of coherent matter.

In upcoming chapters, we'll look at these ideas in greater detail and see how they stack up against the "creepy" cryptid evidence.

The Number One Reason Bigfoot Encounters Aren't Big News

As a former statistics teacher, I think I know the why bigfoot and cryptid encounters aren't considered a serious topic in our society. In statistics, we deal with something called a Normal Distribution. This bell-shaped curved supposedly describes many things in our world that revolve around an average or mean.

For example, human physical heights center on a normal distribution, so does IQ (those researchers in human intelligence are the ones who made the idea of a normal distribution important), and income. However, there's an important caveat here: Many things also don't revolve around the normal distribution, like, for instance, COVID infections which were largely unpredictable from month to month during 2020 and 2021. These infections are based on unknown qualities of the SARS-CO-2 virus itself.

And also how people behave from day to day. These effects are multiplicative and have a completely different statistical distribution. What author Nassim Nicholas Taleb calls "extremistan." Life in extremistan is far from predictable: there are no means and no standard deviations (*The Black Swan,* 2010).

Outliers

However, cryptid and bigfoot encounters are neither of these. They're not normally distributed, nor do they form non-normal distributions as we're familiar with them.

Instead, they're OUTLIERS: rare encounters with no discernible patterns. You never know when you're going to see one or hear cryptid activity, and each encounter seems unique, like a fingerprint. And for that reason, they're completely off our reality radar. We don't even know how to think about them.

When I was a sociology graduate student, we were taught to throw out outliers. That's right: when you encounter a data point that is very dissimilar from other data points in your data set, *you just throw it out*. Why? Because it's ruining your normal distribution, that's why. And all scientists want everything to fit that golden normal distribution, even if reality doesn't literally work that way. It makes your work easier to publish.

And because bigfoot encounters are so unique, just take some time to read about them: they are *all* outliers without any discernible statistical distribution. So they must not exist, right? Wrong. We made the same mistake with COVID vaccines discounting the fact that viruses can and do mutate. Yet, we now admit, we don't what will happen next with the SAR CO-2 virus.

So why exactly do bigfoot encounters have no discernible patterns? I think because they're based on a different type of matter than we're used to, as I argue in the rest of this book.

It's very similar to UFO encounters. For the most part, each event seems unique. You or your relatives could have such a mysterious encounter and then completely forget about it. The features and characteristics of such phenomena are just far out from what your brain is used to. As of this writing, we haven't even had an intelligent discussion on a national level about the subject. Not because it isn't happening, but because it's so different from the norm. And the people who should be discussing it, scientists in their scientific forums, journals, and magazines, won't touch it with a ten-foot pole because it is too far outside their mindset.

Bigfoot and cryptids are just too different from ordinary physical and energetic phenomena that we're used to. So, they mostly stay out of our awareness and conscious dialogue.

But keep this in mind: at one time, airplanes were outliers, too, and people chose to believe that the Wright Brothers were making it all up! Even the US Government refused to fund them, going with astronomer and physicist Samuel Pierpont Langley instead, whose huge flying contraption had to be launched from a houseboat and never, ever worked. *So outliers can go mainstream, at any moment.* Count on it.

Can Academics Tell Us Anything About Cryptids?

Many people think that academics at universities will ultimately tell us the truth about these subjects. As someone who spent many years in a university environment, I highly doubt it. Most academics are more concerned with awards, prestige, and promotions (though there are exceptions) on one the hand or suffer anxiety over being marginalized from their field. The fear of ridicule and going too far astray from their colleagues is an ever-present concern to people who have invested their entire lives in one area of specialization. They become increasingly vulnerable to being ostracized from their profession. End result: They stay away from controversial topics.

For example, take Japanese nuclear science researcher Takaaki Matsumoto, whose research we'll cover in a later chapter. He was told by the American Nuclear Society's *Fusion Science and Technology* journal in 1996 that they would no longer publish his work after he mentioned ball lightning. Thus, the world was deprived of his profound and brilliant writings in the area of cold fusion. Only recently have his profound works been resurrected and published by researcher Robert Greenyer and the folks at the Martin Fleischmann Memorial Project: a non-profit collaboration of volunteers doing cold fusion research. We can wonder how many other researchers in this area were steered away from the subject for fear of rejection by their colleagues or being deprived of ever essential grant money from organizations like the National Science Foundation and other federal science research agencies.

Similarly, recipients of federal science money are limited to who they can talk with if their research is subject to security classifications. As one prominent UFO scientist who worked in AAWSAP (see Chapter 4) bluntly told me about federal grants: "The money is good, but the science isn't."

I remember a professor at one of the universities I went to for graduate school telling me something like this: "You want to be successful in sociology, right? You're investing a lot of time here, yes? Then stick to the mainstream and don't go off studying fringe topics." I'm sure many other grad students get a similar lecture at some point in their careers and are forever scared away from taking risks after that.

But the message is the same: Stick with the program if you want to be accepted by your colleagues and promoted to a full professorship with tenure. By the time you get your Ph. D., It's very rare that any academic, having invested so much time effort and money in their degree will veer off to new subjects with uncertain outcomes. And that would have been my fate, too if, in 1996 I hadn't encountered the subject of the US government remote viewing program. I won't repeat what I wrote in my first book *Opening Minds,* but it was remote viewing that "opened my mind" to a range of topics that I had never considered before including UFOs, orbs, channeling, psychokinesis, telepathy, and crop circles.

So, if we want to understand what's going on with cryptids and other monsters, we must break the norm and go off in new directions with new ideas. Because the ideas we've been using so far haven't gotten us very far apart from debating whether bigfoot is an undiscovered species of ape or an alien from another planet. But neither of these explanations are likely to be accurate because the last time I checked apes don't speak passable English or even a gibberish "reverse samurai" language as Ron Morehead recorded over many trips to the High Sierras in California. And aliens, as far as we know, don't display incredible athletic feats running up hillsides and throwing 500-pound rocks. As I'm about to show you, there is a lot of science you probably haven't heard much about that can tell us about these creatures and similar phenomena.

A New (And Very Old) Type of Matter

We live in a world that is increasingly dominated by technology and technologically mediated events. So much of what we do nowadays is focused on a screen: in our phones, cars, and desks. It could almost lead you to believe that it isn't real if it isn't on a screen. Your favorite news or YouTube channel would mention it, right?

This is a mistaken perspective, in my view. What if the story of reality we were told by society, our teachers, parents, and school systems is complete fiction? What if reality is very different from what we believed it was just a decade ago. And what if government organizations and entities have known about this the whole time and decided not to tell us?

In this book, I will present a case that we are indeed surrounded by mysterious creatures who excel at staying invisible and cloaked and possess extraordinary athletic abilities to boot. So much so that when people encounter these creatures, they have no idea what they're dealing with and no idea how to respond. They often have a PTSD reaction like victims of violent crime: they can't remember any details about what the creature looked like, or their memories of the event seem distorted. Some of the encounters, most of them, are peaceful, and a few are violent, seemingly. And for that reason, we don't often hear about them. Witnesses also describe apparently "paranormal" qualities of these creatures such as levitation, extraordinary travel speeds, telepathy, and Star Trekian "mind melds." These incidents become part of a plethora of "hidden events."

Events like this happen nearly everywhere except in the densest urban areas. They occur in deserts, suburban parking lots, forests, mountains, rivers, plains, and rural and suburban houses. Because of the strangeness of these encounters, witnesses are often quick to judgment, assuming that what they encountered was paranormal, "demonic," alien, or not of this world.

I'm going to argue the opposite here: I'm convinced we're dealing with lifeforms that have long ago adapted to specific energies in the universe that we modern people have shunned. In fact, we're just rediscovering these scientific principles now; principles that are based on the most fundamental of cosmic energetic processes. These processes are called cold fusion, low energy nuclear reaction (LENR), and coherent matter.

So, if we're just rediscovering them now why isn't it possible that other lineages of intelligent creatures figured this all out thousands or hundreds of thousands of years ago. They now live in a different type of space-time than we do, a kind of parallel reality if you wish. What's the evidence?

To start with, almost every aspect of these encounters with cryptid creatures shares similarities with what we know from the modern sciences of Condensed Matter Phenomena. The latter is simply a remarkable state of matter where the sub-atomic particles that make up physical things are pushed together enough so that the particles begin to correlate together. And that correlation produces "strange" effects that make modern electronics possible through quantum tunneling, resonance, and superconductivity. And if you push it far enough, the sub-atomic particles become very similar in frequency and temperature, the particles cluster together, and you create coherent matter.

Once you've created coherent matter, it can do some pretty crazy things like teleportation, cloaking, antigravity, sudden cold, and massive energy bursts. Don't believe me? Just look at the Lockheed Martin patent granted by the US Patent Office in March 2021. They list all these benefits of coherent matter and more.[6] (See Chapter 1)

Do any of these properties seem familiar: sudden cold, teleportation, levitation? Yes, they do. We've seen all of these and more at every paranormal site, location, and event ever mentioned. And there's a reason for this: *Paranormal phenomena and coherent matter are similar things*! Yes, many of the weird things you've heard about concerning haunted sites, cryptid encounters, UFOs, and remote viewing are also seen in labs that study coherent matter from Nikola Tesla to Winston H. Bostick who was funded by the US Air Force in the 1950s. Bostick, who attempted to convert the fusion energy of nuclear weapons into a peaceful source of power, was even the subject of a lengthy *New York Times* article.[7] More recently these results have been seen by the Canadian inventor John Hutchison. We'll get into all of this in subsequent chapters.

It's the nature of the scientific method to simplify things where possible. So why not with these subjects? Einstein once said: "things should be simplified as much as possible . . . but no simpler." I can't think of a subject where this is needed as much as "paranormal phenomena."

Now, suppose you read the conventional literature on superconductivity and coherent matter. You'll be told that these states are only achieved at very low temperatures, when the particles stop moving due to the absence of heat. There's only one problem: it's not true.

There are many ways to create coherent matter at ordinary temperatures, one of which is known as the Aharonov-Bohm Effect: a spooky quantum principle that shows how seemingly separate things can interact macroscopically at a large distance. In fact, it's the stuff of classified military research in the US and probably other countries since the 1950s. The last time I checked, militaries don't fool around: they want stuff that works. And that's why they're studying and researching all of this as we speak. Look at the US Navy labs such as SPAWAR in California, which have been testing a cold fusion apparatus built like the one created by Martin Fleischmann and Stanley Pons, once hailing from the University of Utah, Salt Lake. Their scientific colleagues pilloried and attacked them for their cold fusion experiments, later reproduced by hundreds of labs worldwide. According to Martin Fleischmann, in an interview with Peter Tinsley for Infinite Energy Magazine in 1996, he never wanted to have a press conference to report their results. That idea came from higher-ups at the University of Utah who were eager for a patent claim. Fleischmann said he would have been content to keep researching the subject quietly for many more years.[8]

The essence of the Aharonov-Bohm Effect is Resonance. When all the particles of a particular charge cluster are at the same frequency and temperature, they resonate with one another. Resonance is what drives Cold Fusion and LENR reactions. It's exactly what Vittorio Violante said to the 2015 meeting for the Society for Scientific Exploration in San Francisco. Vittorio said: "Cold fusion is a resonance reaction."[9]

Violante also told us that many researchers attempting to duplicate Fleischmann and Pons had made the mistake of using palladium that was too pure and not having the right grain size. One researcher who successfully reproduced the Fleischmann and Pons experiment was John O'Meara Bockris at Texas A & M University. Bockris was also severely attacked by his university and colleagues for his cold fusion results yet vindicated. His results held up, and he published a book about his experience (*The New Paradigm*, 2013).

To make the reaction successful, the deuterium or hydrogen atoms must be packed tightly in the grain boundaries, not the palladium surface. This tight packing leads to the formation of charge clusters and a resonant feedback loop.

And that *might* be the secret to cryptids, bigfoot, and the like: Resonance. Their bodies are resonating to a novel frequency which would give them access to what to seem like superhuman powers. *The screams and howls are not just for show: they're creating superconducting feedback loops which keep recharging their energy levels.*

Suppose the magic of superconductivity and coherent matter is being studied by defense contractors and aerospace labs are patenting these ideas. Is it plausible that someone or something else didn't already figure it out? Perhaps tens of thousands of years ago, naturally, based on biological and chemical processes already ever-abundant on the Earth? Who said we're the first? If some species of creatures did incorporate these fundamental scientific principles in their biology perhaps they figured out how to do other things we don't easily understand yet. Things like cloaking, ball lightning, orbs, super speeds, ability to drain batteries, zap electronics, and more.

Still with me? Good, let's look deeper.

Chapter 1—The Invisible Universe

"Dirac famously said that he would be 'surprised' if nature had made no use of such an elegant idea as the magnetic monopole."—Nature, "Quantum Cloud Simulates Magnetic Monopole," 2014

When we look out at the skies at night, with the naked eye, we can see thousands of stars and even the Andromeda Galaxy if we're in a dark area. Yet, modern cosmology tells us that we can only see a small fraction of all the matter, perhaps a few percent at most. It seems counterintuitive, yet up to a whopping 34 percent of our physical universe is suspected to be a mysterious substance called dark matter (and the most of the remainder is dark energy, the force that pushes galaxies apart). Although some physicists have attempted to explain it away as a mathematical aberration needing no additional particles or energies, none of these approaches have succeeded. This means that the race is still on to figure what this dark stuff actually is made of.

Speculations about the existence of dark matter go all the way back to Greek philosophers, one of whom, Philolaus, suggested that there was a "mirror Earth," which he called *Antichthon.* Another Greek philosopher, Epicurus, imagined there were "an infinite number of worlds." And it is Galileo who is credited with discovering previously unobserved matter with his telescope, the glow of the Milky Way, and moons which orbited Jupiter, which could not be seen with the naked eye. Inspired by Copernicus and Galileo, the natural philosopher Giordano Bruno expanded on these ideas. He was burned at the stake in 1640 in part for his beliefs in an infinite universe full of lifeforms we hadn't encountered yet.

John Michell is credited with having invented the idea of invisible matter in 1784 with his suggestions of stars from which light could not escape: black holes. Karl Schwarzchild resurrected such an idea in 1916 based on Einstein's General Relativity. Schwarzchild argued that black holes would warp space-time and produce a "singularity": a place where things seemingly went to infinite values beyond the black hole's "event horizon." In such a space, even light would not be able to escape. And in 1931, Subrahmanyan Chandrasekhar showed stars or objects above a certain mass would necessarily collapse into a black hole. Some physicists opposed this idea at the time, like Eddington and Landau, and even Einstein, whose theories predicted such an object, couldn't imagine that such a thing as a black hole could exist. According to Einstein, such an idea was "not convincing" and did not exist in "the real world." In fact, it wasn't until recently in 2019, that a black hole was actually photographed in the galaxy Messier 87.

Belief in the idea of dark matter was also slow historical development. Lord Kelvin in 1884, suggested that the mass of stars, as he could calculate back then, was not sufficient to explain their rotational speed around the center of the galaxy. Kelvin referred to these objects as "dark bodies," which was later interpreted as "dark matter," or "mati`ere obscure," by mathematician

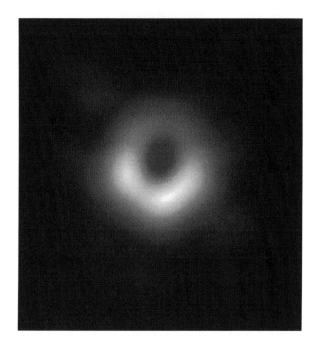

Fig. 5. First ever Photographed Black Hole in 2019
(Image by EHT Collaboration)

Henry   Poincare   in   1906.   Dark
matter was invoked to explain particularities in the
orbits of Jupiter before Uranus was discovered. Others
scientists as Jacobus Kapteyn, Jan Oort, and Knut
Lundmark suggested similar ideas. However, Swiss-
American astronomer Fritz Zwicky officially discovered
the idea in 1933, and it was later verified by Vera Rubin
in 1972. Dark matter is invisible to the eye and only
detectable by its gravitational influences on ordinary,
visible matter and it does not interact with normal
matter through electromagnetic means.

According to astrophysicist Joel Primack, there are
10 invisible particles in our universe for every visible
one. And when you include dark energy (the force
pushing galaxies apart) and non-luminous matter (so-
called non-baryonic particles), you're left with only *one-
half of one percent* of our universe that is visible. The
vast majority of our universe is still invisible to us.

Fig. 6. Representation of Dark Matter in Our Universe.
(Image by NASA)

A growing consensus is emerging, however, from organizations like CERN and NASA, that a small part of what makes up dark matter are what is called "Relic Neutrinos": tiny, energetic subatomic particles that emerged a second after the Big Bang and separated from the rest of the particles in the cosmos. This idea of original neutrinos from the Big Bang was initially proposed by Russian cosmologist Zeldovich in 1966. These particles are slow enough and large enough to interact with us through our atomic particles and biological cells. Even though we can't detect relic neutrinos directly, we can measure their influence on subatomic activity, variations in biological processes, and galactic correlations. For example, Russian scientists like Simon Schnoll of Moscow State University have long noticed mysterious variations in radioactive decay in atoms, chemical processes like the clockwork-like Belousov-Zhabotinsky reaction, seed germination rates, and noise in electronic components like diodes.[10]

Relic neutrinos differ from those emitted by the Sun which is much smaller and faster, rarely interacting with ordinary matter. We're told that, on average, it would take a minuscule solar neutrino ten years of linear motion in solid lead before it would collide with a lead atom. Relic neutrinos, having a larger wavelength, on the other hand, would interact with atoms, organisms, and biology, all over the planet and everywhere they exist, which is the entire universe.

Paul Dirac's Antimatter Universe

By studying the ideas of quantum mechanics, Paul Dirac, who later shared a Nobel Prize in 1933 with Erwin Schrödinger, argued that the Quantum Wave Function implied the existence of alternative mathematical solutions and a mirror universe of antiparticles. With his now famous Dirac Equation, he was able to show that quantum mechanics and Einstein's relativity required the existence of a universe of invisible antiparticles for every particle we know of. In other words, antimatter. This idea of a "mirror world" has even inspired modern physicists like Leah Broussard to begin tests looking for a "parallel Earth" at Oak Ridge National Laboratory.[11] And one of the key findings of this possible parallel "mirrorverse" is that it would be colder than our own.

The idea of a mirror, parallel Earth is based on the discrepancy of neutron decay rates. Neutrons outside of an atomic nucleus decay at different rates depending on how you set up your experiments. There are no straightforward explanations for these varying measurements. The measurements for neutron decay should be exactly the same. One possibility is that particles we know of in our world may be spending brief moments in a parallel reality and then returning to our world, kind of like a grand time-sharing arrangement.[12] This is also found in the substance scientists call "Positronium"—a short-lived particle made of an electron and a positron. Decay rates for Positronium are a bit shorter than they should be, suggesting they are spending some of their time in a parallel reality.

Scientists speculate that this mirror universe would only interact with ours gravitationally.[13] More evidence for this mirror universe came in the 1950s discovery by physicists Lee and Yang at Brookhaven National Labs, for which they won a Nobel Prize. They found that neutrinos in our universe only have a left-handed spin creating an asymmetry that has yet to be explained.

The Never-Ending Quest for Hot Fusion

Around the world, scientists for decades have attempted to create Hot Fusion, a supposed replica of what happens on the Sun, where Hydrogen continually fuses to create Helium. Until recently, they've only been able to do this for a trillionth of a second because it's challenging to confine such a high-temperature reaction. And of the writing of this book, the new time record for sustaining such a reaction has been extended to a few seconds before the magnetic field containing the incredibly hot reaction breaks down.

But what if such a reaction is already in nature all around us, sustaining life at every moment invisibly? What if a colder version of fusion already exists, right here, right now, in your body and every living thing around you? What if creatures on our planet in the distant past had learned to harness this energy source and its benefits? And they had evolved over time into different species, some familiar, others unrecognizable? And what if these creatures are still here, roaming the Earth, having integrated the energy of relic neutrinos and the secrets of dark matter into their physiology?

What if these creatures had an ambivalent relationship with modern humans, sometimes benign, at other times predatory? Would they not seem to us like Dark Matter Monsters?

Precursors to Dark Matter Energy Systems

Serbian-American inventor Nikola Tesla experimented with novel electrical systems, created AC power, alternating current as we know it, fluorescent light bulbs, and toyed with inventions, like a remote controlled submarines (all the way back in the 1890s), and others that he saw in his imagination but never saw the light of day, like self-powered airplanes. Tesla repeatedly said that all his technologies were based on resonance, frequency, vibration and energy all around us in nature. Think this is too vague and metaphysical? Hardly. In 2021, Canadian researcher David Boutilier reproduced Tesla's technology from reading Tesla's papers written in Colorado Springs. Boutilier created not only waves of plasma and arc electricity but also *tiny ball lightning* right there in his lab surrounding the equipment. Just like Tesla reported. (See this video on lab-produced ball lightning: (https://youtu.be/y1-aMp9oJtk)).

So why is ball lightning so important? I'll sum it up for you in a nutshell: It's a Macroscopic Coherent Quantum Object. What does that mean? The electrons give up their individual identities and behave as one big particle instead. From this perspective, ball lightning is essentially one big electron; until it breaks down and the individual electrons acquire their particular temperatures and frequencies again.

Once electrons are pressurized through one of many means and form a charge cluster, their natural tendency to repel each other is overcome by the opposite property: they're intensely attracted to each other (precisely at 10^{-13} meters, if you're curious). So what we were taught in textbooks about the finality of Coulombic Repulsion is not a complete description of clustered electrons' behavior at very high densities.[14] The electrostatic repulsive principle that usually keeps electrons apart is overcome by an overwhelming strong, attractive magnetic force, and the electrons bunch up into strings, toroids, and rings. Viola! Mini ball lightning. That may be a bit of an oversimplification, but not by much. Nature is fully capable of creating exotic states of clustered matter with seemingly novel and unexpected energetic properties. And that's just the beginning.

Coherent Matter and the Ghostly Aharonov-Bohm Effect

In 2013, one of the world's largest aerospace companies, Lockheed Martin, filed for a patent in "Coherent Matter Wave Beam" technology.[15] This is not the experimental mini-sized hot fusion reactor they patented in 2018, a shrunk-down version of those giant, complex fusion machines that make a lot of headlines. Instead, Coherent Matter technology is designed to create a uniform, large-scale organization of particles that can project energy across large distances using a mysterious quantum property called the Aharonov-Bohm Effect. In March of 2021, the US Patent Office approved the patent.

The Aharonov-Bohm effect, discovered in the 1950s, states that electromagnetic energy is transmitted from the quantum realm, even if nothing is measurable from a classical standpoint. So if you measure a space near a completely shielded magnet, and the magnetism in that space is zero, meaning absolutely no magnetic force there at all, there will be some magnetism coming from the "ghost waves" of quantum activity, so-called "vector potential." Thus, there is some "flux leakage" from the quantum realm. In other words, the potential energy of a system described by the Schrödinger Quantum Wave Function, a purely mathematical construction containing imaginary numbers, actually describes something with real physical consequences in our world. And this was experimentally verified by researcher Akira Tonomura at Hitachi Labs in 1986. The implications of this discovery are immense.

It tells us that alternative quantum states of matter that we can't literally see or detect in any ordinary way are still affecting our reality. In effect, we're interacting with ghost realities.

Coherent Matter isn't new: it's seen in the Bose-Einstein Condensates (BECS). These are coherent groups of atoms at extremely cold temperatures that were theorized to exist by Einstein and Bose in the 1930s and then finally seen in 1999 at the federal government's NIST facility in Boulder, Colorado.

However, BECS and most superconducting systems require cold temperatures near absolute zero to date. Room-temperature superconductivity is seen from time to time in substances like graphene. It is something that researchers in this subject area are constantly striving for: Creating superconductivity at room temperatures. Because once you can create superconducting materials, the electronic efficiency of those devices goes way up, and they become exponentially more efficient.

Lockheed Martin claimed they could create Coherent Matter Beams at any temperature, hot or cold: it didn't matter. It's like a laser, which is coherent light, only millions of times stronger. They said you could create directed energy weapons, cloaking, missile defense, and control over distant objects with that technology. You get the idea: new types of super weapons and technologies operating on quantum principles.

This wasn't Lockheed Martin's first foray into matter manipulation and gravity reduction. In 2014, one of their researchers, Boyd Bushman, applied for a patent to use directed magnetic beams to create gravitational effects. And he reiterated that galactic dark matter here on Earth could be organized coherently. Dark matter could interact with the ordinary matter we're familiar with. According to Bushman:

> Well, there is another universe called the neutrino universe, of course. We know that it's there, and now we're seeing if one of the additional forces matches it. Not only that, we know that everything that we see is about 5 percent and then there's 70 percent dark energy . . . and that's what we're talking about.[16]

So, what exactly is Coherent Matter? Well, think of it this way: Ordinary matter consists of atomic and sub-atomic particles at different frequencies and temperatures that make up our bodies' chemical and physical properties and everything around us. The book or computer you're reading right now; the walls of the room or car you're in; the planet, the atmosphere, almost everything. The diversity of particle properties allows them to hold the material world together and perform predictably in our electronic equipment.

But even in electronic equipment, they do this at the substantial cost of producing lots of heat because the electrons don't flow smoothly through metals but are constantly bouncing off every atom they run into. Which is why your electronic devices phones or laptop computers get warm to the touch.

However, let's say the sub-atomic particles that make up life and living things, carbon, oxygen, sulfur, and all the elements in the periodic table, were turned temporarily into identical particles like uniform soldiers in an army. And all the electrons are now at the same temperature and frequency. This is called monochromaticity: they've lost any identity as specific elements in the periodic table and become a type of primal matter that can be literally anything. Under the proper circumstances, you'd end up with one big, glowing yet cool to the touch particle: A ball of light!

And that cluster of particles would behave according to different rules than ordinary matter. It would be able to cloak; it would be able to float; it would be able to teleport.

And when that ball of magic matter, the charge cluster, comes apart, all the electrons will rejoin the original particles. The electrons become incoherent again, all going their separate ways, and resume their individual identities ABSORBING energy from their environment. So when the charge cluster comes apart, it will get icy cold in the surrounding area. It will get darn chilly!

Well, guess what? Isn't that people and researchers report near UFOs, haunted houses, poltergeists, and bigfoot? A sudden chill? I'll answer that for you. Yes: that's exactly what is reported around those phenomena.

Coherent Matter Lifeforms

If Lockheed Martin can get a patent in Coherent Matter, it's real, right? I mean, colossal aerospace companies don't dabble around in things that don't exist. However, let's say they didn't invent it. Perhaps, although the idea is new to us "modern" folk, nature has been doing this for a long, long time: creating living systems that can produce enough microscopic coherency to glide, float, teleport, and even transmute chemical elements. It might seem like the paranormal or magic to us, but these phenomena would seem ordinary to those familiar with them.

And if nature has been doing this for a long, long time, who's to say that lifeforms on Earth haven't figured out a way to use these seemingly magical processes themselves in their day-to-day lives. Yes, I'm talking cloaking, teleportation, fantastic displays of energetic power, etc. And that's what we see with bigfoot and a host of other cryptid creatures like dogman, goatman, the Thunderbird of Native American culture, and perhaps some creatures we haven't even heard of yet or don't have a name for.

While we're on the subject, it's unclear if dogman is a distinct species or a sub-species of bigfoot, as Lapseritis argues.[17] I spoke with a store owner in Westcliffe, Colorado, who knew some witnesses. The descriptions are remarkably consistent: a bipedal creature with a human-like torso and a head that looks like a German Shepard. Some witnesses, at first, think they see a human in a Halloween dog costume. Then they realize it's not a costume. In one case, the creature swam across a river; in the other, it walked right past some people, stunned by the sight of the creature, on a dirt road right outside of town.

If you've read anything about bigfoot, you're aware that there are widely divergent views on exactly what the creature is. Some people see it as an undiscovered ape, an anthropoid, from the past: Gigantopithecus, though there is no evidence it walked on two legs. Or perhaps a type of ancient human, or even a human-ape hybrid. A century ago, they were referred to *as escaped*

Fig. 7. Representation of Gigantopithecus. There is no Evidence it Walked on two legs or Migrated to North America. (Image by Concavenator, CC4.0)[18]

gorillas, wild men, or hairy men because no one had any idea what they were.

There is a report from Moscow Mountain in Idaho from an incident in the 60s, near where I went to graduate school at Washington State University in Pullman, Washington. The witnesses were a child who climbed a tree while his father was chopping wood. A few minutes before, both father and child had the feeling of being watched. The child climbed a tree and said what looked like a "monkey" crawled up the tree after him and was only 8 inches from his face: the child then let out a "blood curdling" scream out of fear, and the creature went into the brush and disappeared. They also noticed that the cows grazing up in that area seemed edgy and nervous. Later the father searched the area for traveling circuses thinking a monkey might have escaped. There was no indication any circus had been in the area at any time in the recent past. (http://www.bfro.net/GDB/show_report.asp?id=6758)

But you also have others say that this "flesh and blood" approach is insufficient to explain the weird phenomena around bigfoot or geographic dispersion: they're seen in every state, including Hawaii (based on anecdotal reports). This weirdness includes balls of light, orbs, glowing eyes, and the ability for the creature to teleport, project thoughts into your head, run as fast as a jet, or disappear instantly.

I'm going to take a stab at what's going on here: I believe these cryptids can interact with dark matter, the substance that scientists say makes up as much as ten times as much mass as ordinary matter. And dark matter can do strange things, like form clusters that create anomalous energy spheres, tunnel through solid surfaces, and even generate superconductivity at room temperature. And if such creatures exist in our world, they would seemingly have what we would perceive as superpowers that we humans don't think they possess (at least not yet). These creatures would have another power source that ordinary humans don't know is there. And this power source would be very similar to what we call cold fusion or Low Energy Nuclear Reaction (LENR): In other words, coherent matter.

The thesis of the book is simple: I believe at the heart of every phenomenon we call "paranormal" is, in fact, coherent matter and related processes. Coherent matter can create cloaking, transmutation, teleportation, and ball lightning. As we'll see, it happens in the microscopic processes of Low Energy Nuclear Reactions, previously known as cold fusion, as studied by researchers Fleischmann and Pons at the University of Utah, and in macroscopic phenomena like ball lightning. And in ghosts, hauntings, bigfoot, shapeshifters, UFOs, and everything in between. We're talking about a scientific tradition with over one hundred years of experiments and research. It only seems weird because we haven't ever had much of a discussion about it since the days of Nicola Tesla.

Bigfoot in My Graduate Career (or Not)

When I was a graduate student at Washington State University in Pullman, WA, in the late 1980s and early 90s, there was a member of the anthropology department in the same building, Wilson Hall. Grover Krantz was one of the few academics in the US to take the Bigfoot/Sasquatch phenomena seriously. He believed it was an elusive, undiscovered ape: Gigantopithecus perhaps. And in 1989, a Bigfoot conference was held at WSU. I didn't know about this conference or Grover Krantz, even though we might have passed each other in the stairwell or the elevator. Back then, I don't think I would have been interested. It was just too far from my college and graduate training in social sciences. Yet here we are 30 years later, and my views couldn't have changed more.

Going Down the Rabbit Hole?

Many folks think this is a "going down the rabbit hole" topic. You'll go in but never come out. However, I don't believe we are in danger of doing so. Just the opposite: there are too many good witnesses and sightings from worldwide. In a court of law, witness testimony under oath is strong evidence. People can be convicted of serious crimes based on witness testimony. And I think we have a lot of evidence from many witnesses.

At a recent meeting in Bailey, Colorado, in 2022, researcher and explorer Jim Myers of the Sasquatch Outpost said that based on the BFRO.net map of encounters, there may have been over 100,000 encounters since BFRO started recording these several decades ago.19

The topic is not easy to come to terms with, but people were also skeptical back in the early 1900s when Mountain Gorillas were rediscovered. I doubt bigfoot is an undiscovered ape or an ordinary yet rare animal: it's more complex than that. But who said the entire universe has to fit into our preconceived paradigms? Neither did black holes, quasars, continental drift, the human subconscious, or quasicrystals. It's just how reality works: its definition and scope change from century to century. Should it be any different now?

The Scientific Method

Our modern idea of science is based on explaining the most facts with the fewest assumptions and theories. However, it wasn't always like that. Natural philosophers, as they were called, weren't interested in falsifying or supporting theories. They simply wanted to explain how the strictest ideas of Aristotle and the medieval Church were true, not whether there was any data at all to support those viewpoints. Looking at the data itself is a new idea that is particular to the modern era. And in this case, the data support the notion of cryptids: hidden creatures that defy easy categorization and fall outside the bounds of accepted science. Whether that fits easily into our modern way of thinking is another question.

When I speak to some educated people about this subject, they sometimes tell me the witnesses are "delusional." Sure, and so were Galileo, Copernicus,

Faraday, and Einstein. This criticism has been leveled at anyone with a different view of reality than the mainstream: even cosmologists talking about dark matter. And the last time I checked, ridicule isn't part of the scientific method. We need to develop a better reaction than that, rather than just second-guessing the witnesses. And my first choice would be to say that it's our social beliefs that are delusional and out of whack with reality. It wouldn't be the first time this has been the case.

What you're going to read in the rest of this book may seem like science fiction. However, as Robert Heinlein said: "today's science fiction is tomorrow's science." At one time, the Wright Brother's flying machines seemed like science fiction, and everyone made fun of them, including the *New York Times*. But that's because our mindset is always lagging behind reality. And so it is with cryptids, UFOs, and other paranormal phenomena. They may seem like science fiction, unbelievable, a product of delusional thinking. But that's what people have always said about technologies and science now part of our everyday lives. Because electricity, magnetism, and vacuums inside glass bottles were also once considered supernatural.[20]

Chapter 2— "What You Saw Was a Bear": Sociocultural Stigma and Why People Don't Report Encounters with the Unexplained Phenomena

"This is our career, we can t have weird stuff that we have to explain to our superiors." —Police officer responding to bigfoot sighting in York County, Pennsylvania[21]

"If I told you and word got out, it would ruin my reputation. I m not going to say what I think it might be, but let's just say it's not human and it's not a regular-type mammal." —Member of Flathead County, Montana sheriff's Search and Rescue group to Glacier National Park ranger[22]

I'm always amazed by the type of comments above, of the number of people who choose to remain silent about what they've encountered, out of their concern for job security, in law enforcement, the military, or emergency first-responders. The pressure to appear "normal" and "sane" to one's colleagues usually outweighs the necessity of reporting unusual lifeforms or experiences that one has encountered. I'm not criticizing such a response but want to point out that if this type of behavior is typical of people who have met cryptids up "close and personal," decades could go by without the subject being taken seriously. And this conflict of interest has not gone unnoticed by the US government.

The UAP Task Force Report

In June of 2021, the UAP Task Force report, ordered by the Senate Subcommittee on Intelligence a year before, identified "sociocultural stigma" as a barrier to gathering information about the UFO phenomenon. Another hearing on the subject, this time in front of a House Committee reached the same conclusion:

> For too long the stigma associated with UAPs has gotten in the way of good intelligence analysis. Pilots avoided reporting or were laughed at when they did. DOD officials relegated the issue to the back room or swept it under the rug entirely, fearful of a skeptical national security community.[23]

Navy pilots had reported strange encounters with unidentified objects in military practice areas for decades. Still, many pilots were afraid to talk about it. Talking about such sightings could impair their military careers. While the Nimitz Encounters of 2004 or Roosevelt incidents in 2015 were known from the New York Times and Politico articles from December 2017, how many other cases were there? How many other witnesses had yet to come forward? Without accurate witness reports of UFOs, the subject will continually slip below the radar of social consciousness.

Until recently, people referred to the whole middle part of America that didn't touch the coasts as "flyover country." It's the part of the US that you'd fly over going from New York to the West Coast. Until George Bush won the Presidential Election in 2000 by successfully organizing in states like Ohio, the mass media considered these areas of the country to be irrelevant to mainstream life, at least politically. No one calls these states "flyover country" anymore because even smaller states can now swing presidential elections; it's not enough to win big, urbanized states like California and New York.

And because of this attitude by coastal urban people towards their more rural, interior neighbors, we've ignored a lot of data and encounter-cases over the years from places like Montana, Ohio, Arizona, and Missouri. This attitude reinforced the belief that only alcoholic, isolated, rural people had UFO sightings. The same attitude characterizes cryptid encounters, and these events haven't been taken seriously by and large. And East and West Coast university academics could continue to perpetuate the idea that cryptids were simply the stuff of urban legend and folklore. And to paraphrase, one academic from the University of California Berkeley said in a recent interview in their alumni magazine: "it's rational for people to believe in modern folklore like bigfoot because it helps them fit into their local cultural milieu."[27] From this point of view, belief in cryptids is a coping mechanism that rural people employ to help them relate to other rural people.

This overly simplistic, prejudiced attitude, which I also heard expressed by one of my high school social science teachers in the 70s, is one of the main reasons we know so little about cryptids. It could be ignored quite easily with little negative repercussion on your career. In my entire education career, from kindergarten to Ph.D. in 1993, I never heard a single serious mention of UFOs, bigfoot, psychic functioning, psychokinesis, or any related phenomena even though I grew up near the Hudson Valley, NY, where huge triangular-shaped craft were seen starting in the late 1970s. And yet the famous Patterson-Gimlin footage, filmed in Bluff Creek, CA, happened in 1967. And a few years later, Ron Morehead started recording his amazing Sierra Sounds in the early 1970s, which he continued doing for many years. Yes, one could dismiss both as hoaxes, but where's the scientific method here: a counter-point of view looking at the solidity of this evidence?

In the language of American sociologist William Fielding Ogburn, one could argue that lack of serious analysis of this type of evidence is a type of "cultural lag." Our scientific culture must catch up to the evidence like we are catching up with the decades of ignored UFO evidence.

As Kelleher and Knapp wrote in *Hunt for the Skinwalker*: "The scientific establishment does not look kindly upon professionals who stray too far from what are deemed legitimate areas of study."[28]

The Cultural Divide

In my view, these urbanites are just insulating themselves from reality. They are as wrong about bigfoot as they were about predicting the presidential election of George Bush in 2000 or especially Donald Trump in 2016. Academics live in a bubble of their own making and can't conceive that their models, theories, and predictions could be wrong. So they're entirely missing this phenomenon except those like Grover Krantz, now deceased, or Jeff Meldrum and a few other brave souls. But the pressure amongst the modern literati to conform to a debunking mentality, also with UFOs, is intense. And that's why we're mostly out of touch with reality: The reality of Dark Matter Lifeforms.

And there's another thing that UFO researcher Jacques Vallee has said many times: "the stranger the story, the less likely witnesses are to talk about it." So experiences involving missing time, electronics failure, and general "weirdness" can be dismissed even by the witnesses themselves, and they won't tell ANYONE. So we end up with a severe bias in data reporting, which distorts our view of reality even more.

For example, a college biology student was a witness in Chautauqua Park in Boulder County, Colorado. He had his sighting in 1995, according to the BFRO website but did not report it for ten years for fear of ridicule! He was up at the park, just at the edge of town, at 11 PM. He saw a large, tall human-like figure covered in hair standing up just before him. "It looked like a very large, hairy, naked person with a powerful build, broad shoulders, and a relatively small, pointed or bullet-shaped head" He also said it ran with "hunched-over, loping gait." Sound familiar? (http://bfro.net/GDB/show_report.asp?id=13411)

Fig. 8. Area in Chautauqua Mountain Park Where College Student saw a Hairy, Hunched, Bipedal Creature at Night. (Photo by Author)

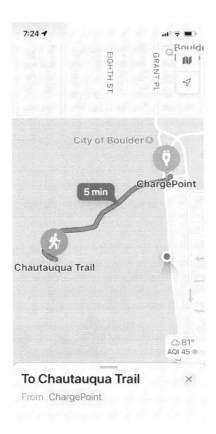

Fig. 9. Map Showing area
Bigfoot Sighting Near the
Chautauqua Parking Lot.
(Image ©2022 by Apple Maps)

We must wonder how many other people like this biology student are not reporting what they've seen. The BFRO site lists over 5,000 encounter cases, all followed up by BFRO trained investigators, of varying types, including visual sightings, footprints, tree knocking sounds, etc. Suppose only one in ten witnesses are reporting these incidents to the BFRO. In that case, that will put the actual number of witnesses at over 50,000 in the US alone. If only one in twenty witnesses, then that number would be over 100,000 people.

The Giggle Factor

Recently, there was an episode on the podcast *Sasquatch Chronicles* entitled "A Whirlwind of Weirdness." [27] The witness, Cindy from Virginia, described how her home was near the edge of a large forest. While her job had kept her from being home, she had stopped traveling so much and had more time to spend in the house. Her husband was occupied with jobs around Washington, DC, so she had a lot of time by herself in her previously vacant home. At first, she started hearing screams and howls coming from the woods behind her house. Then she heard creatures slapping the sides of her house, jumping up onto her veranda 14ft. above the ground and generally making a racket at all hours of the night. One day, in conversation with her neighbors, they asked her about the strange sounds coming from the forest. When she suggested it was caused by Sasquatch, they mockingly laughed at her. As a result, she never brought the subject up again to anyone in her neighborhood, even though all the residents were probably hearing the same sounds coming from the woods that abutted their backyards.

A man who took my RV classes in Boulder had a similar experience in the 1970s. He recently told me that he was in 9th grade at the time of the sighting. He and his dad were driving at night between Deckers and Woodland Park in Colorado. Suddenly, they saw a giant, bipedal creature, darkish in color, some eight to nine feet tall, cross the road ahead of them. "It crossed the two-lane state highway in just two and a half steps and then stepped over a four-foot-high barbed wire fence without slowing down," he told me. "Its legs were as long as most people are tall." His dad insisted it was a bear and never wanted to talk about it again. The dad was unusually quiet when they got home and said nothing about it to the witness's mother. After some inquiries from his mother about his dad's silence that night, he finally confessed to what they had seen. He said she looked dazed and shocked for a few moments, "like a deer in headlights," but probably understood since she had heard bigfoot stories in their hometown of Duluth, Minnesota. About a year later, the witness

Fig. 10. Area of Bigfoot Sighting near Woodland Park, Colorado
(Image © 2022 by Apple Maps)

told a trusted friend at high school about the incident. Soon all the other kids started making fun of him mercilessly, calling him "Hey, Mr. Bigfoot." He remembers one phrase: "You're so full of sh*t, you weird mother f*cker." This harassment lasted for two months, and the witness regretted ever mentioning the sighting to anyone.

I think that at least half of the "weirdness factor" of this topic is not the subject itself: the issue goes against social convention and our definitions of reality.

There was a time when Alfred Wegener's idea of continental drift in the 1910s encountered the same reaction. It wasn't until researcher Marie Tharp, working at Columbia University in the 1960s, created irrefutable evidence of tectonic movement, by creating underwater maps of the oceans showing valleys and other features, that scientists started taking Wegener's ideas seriously. As one of Tharp's colleagues said: "I discounted it as girl talk and didn't believe it for a year."[28] People needed a mechanism to explain plate tectonics before believing in it.

And the same type of thing happened to our understanding of intelligence. At one time, intelligence was thought to be 100 percent inherited from parents. The psychology department at UCLA was particularly vociferous about this point of view and attacked any academic with an opposing perspective. This happened to the Iowa Welfare Unit, the state's department for children's welfare. After placing some previously mentally disabled children in foster homes, they noticed their intelligence had increased. Environment indeed made a difference in children's development. Yet, the UCLA folks still opposed them because they were wedded to the idea of intelligence being entirely heritable and having nothing to do with "nurture" and environment.

We've seen that both plate tectonics and the nature of children's intelligence were so controversial. Why should it be any different with cryptids? With UFOs? Or with psychic functioning? New discoveries in science are often, if not always, ridiculed and opposed. The adherents of these new ideas are often subject to attack. Because this is the human condition, or at least it has been, witnesses to previously unexplained and unaccepted phenomena are unlikely to come forward without great incentives.

However, suppose we can show that so-called "paranormal phenomena" are connected in some way to a novel type of matter with exotic properties. In that case, it becomes easier to accept and talk about. In the same way, the national discussion of UFOs became suddenly more accessible after they were referred to as "UAPs." Though the new terminology doesn't necessarily tell us anything more about them, it seemingly and magically removes the stigma associated with the subject matter. Professionals and scientists can finally talk about it without fear of losing their jobs. At the same time, moving away from calling them "objects" or "vehicles" to "phenomena" instead does not actually advance our knowledge of what they are. And several hundred years ago, scientists of the day argued against relabeling all unknowns as "phenomena" for precisely this reason: it didn't advance our knowledge of what those unknowns are. [29]

A Hole in Modern Science

This all suggests that if people are experiencing phenomena they can't or won't talk about, sometimes ever again, we won't have a way to scientifically study it. And that means the scientific method won't work because we don't have a consistent data source. Suppose the witnesses have PTSD from their encounters. In that case, we'll have a hole in science because there won't be enough data and information reported to know what's going on.

The long-run result of this situation will be what Hal Puthoff calls a "Sputnik Moment": where we realize we have fallen behind another society in technological and scientific understanding. And who's to say this hasn't already happened. A recent blurb in Science Magazine noted that the US has already fallen behind other countries in some fields of science.

In an article by former DoD official Chris Mellon in the *TheDebrief.org,* "Is the Air Force Hiding Something?" he said this about the stigma Air Force pilots face from reporting UFOs: "The apparent lack of

Air Force pilot and radar operator UAP reporting suggests a dangerously dysfunctional culture that is effectively blinding our personnel to potential new threats."[30]

He lists all the myriad electronic surveillance systems available to the US Air Force that should have shown them the same UAP/UFOs that the Navy reported in 2004, 2015, and most recently in 2019. These included swarms of small craft around the USS Omaha, USS Kid, and USS Kearsarge, among other ships in the SOCAL fleet doing exercises off the coast of San Diego.

I would argue that the same stigma applies to the US National Park and Forest Services. Their park rangers, biologists, and other personnel are discouraged from reporting any type of bigfoot or cryptid sightings or encounters. Doing so wouldn't be "career-enhancing." And from what I've read, the bosses at those organizations tell their employees to "forget about it" or "you saw a bear" if they know what's good for them. So these terrified employees choose silence over openness. As a result, campers and hikers go into known areas of cryptid activity, at least known to the park service, without any preparation. We're told that some don't come back.

I'm familiar with this attitude when my dog Jasper and I encountered a mother moose, and her hidden offspring smack dab in the middle of a national forest campground where we had stopped for lunch in early Spring some years ago outside of Teton National Park. The adult moose suddenly charged my leashed dog, who I quickly let go of as I ran for a tree to climb. The moose chased my dog around for what seemed like quite a while. We were OK in the end and made it back to the safety of my truck. The moose was eyeing us coldly as we left. Stopping in the next ranger station I found, I asked why they didn't have a sign in the campground about the moose situation. I was simply and bluntly told: "moose kill dogs all the time." That was it. This attitude told me the National Forest employees didn't care a hoot about my safety while using their campgrounds. I doubt it's any different with bigfoot, dogman, or anything else that is out there on the vast acres of US government property. If you disappeared out there, they wouldn't even blink.

According to researcher David Paulides, who has many books and the *Canam Missing* YouTube channel devoted to the subject, this is the case. He studies missing persons in national parks and forests. The government organizations that have jurisdictions over these areas will do anything to avoid discussing this issue. Yosemite National Park alone has over 100 cases of recent, mysterious human disappearances. Similar unexplained cases of missing people also happen in other National Parks, including Glacier and Yellowstone. Typically, Search and Rescue teams, spotting planes, and trained dogs are brought in to no avail. Sometimes not a single clue is ever found. Even stranger, occasionally intact bodies are found days or weeks later in areas that had already been repeatedly searched or at the tops of nearby mountains or ridges.

I'm familiar with this kind of case from my contact with a former attorney, federal prosecutor, and author Terry Lovelace, author of *Incident at Devil's Den: A True Story*.[31] The book is about his strange contact while camping with an Air Force buddy, with a giant, triangular craft near Devil's Den State Park in Arkansas. Though they were eventually released from the ship with unexplained burn-type injuries a few hours later, Lovelace found out that this area has a long history of missing persons. Predictably, his Air Force superiors did everything possible to prevent him from ever talking about the event again, including contacting his buddy, Toby. He was also taken into the craft that night. Toby, unfortunately, died several years later, apparently from alcoholism and stress related to the incident.

Terry told me that he recently received a call from an investigator at the Dept. of Homeland Security. This individual wanted to know all about Terry and Toby's encounter at Devil's Den. Terry told him the entire UFO abduction story, every detail. When Terry was done recounting his tale, the investigator then told him that DHS was taking these incidents seriously and was launching a criminal investigation into who the perpetrators might be. When Terry joked that he didn't believe the US federal government had any legal jurisdiction over extraterrestrials there was no response on the other end of the phone line, just silence. Terry inferred from this conversation that there might be humans involved in some of these events.

UFO Silence at Minot Air Force Base

I can relate to this stress. A few years after publishing *Black Swan Ghosts*, I interviewed a former Air Force security guard named Gary whose job was to patrol the nuclear Minuteman missile launch facilities of Minot Air Force Base. One night he and his colleague were ordered to repeatedly check on an alarm in a missile site near Velva, North Dakota. The second time around that evening, they encountered a huge, blindingly bright object near the silo. It was so bright they couldn't even distinguish its shape. As the object rose straight up in the air, they had to shield their eyes and later suffered burns on the right side of their bodies. Even the Security Alert Team jeep was burned on the right side, as were weapons and objects inside the vehicle.

The next day the Air Force separated the two guards and told them never to see or talk to one another again. Gary remembers being told that talking to the press "wouldn't be a good idea." The Air Force attempted to hypnotize Gary to get him to reveal more details about the event and then forget about it. Gary ended up suffering long-term medical consequences, on the right side of his body, from this encounter which he is still suffering from. The VA claims to have "lost" his medical records and insists that he now pays for his own medical care. (Readers can watch the interview on my YouTube channel.)

So, it appears that the double-whammy of stigma and bureaucratic intransigence combine to prevent a realistic discussion of any of these phenomena. I've previously referred to these topics as "Social Danger Zones." Even the organization NICAP was reluctant to investigate strange cases of contact. As Gordon Lore said in the previously mentioned report: "NICAP is still somewhat dubious about the authenticity of such bizarre reports as the ones just presented here."

I've known two civilian pilots over the years, both of whom worked for United Airlines. One of them had been in the Air Force in the 1950s before working for United and shared some UFO stories for my book *Black Swan Ghosts*. The other was, for a while, the youngest Boeing 777 pilot in United. They both told me that reporting a UFO sighting as a civilian pilot for a major airline would bring significant grief in terms of a fitness evaluation and possibly a psychiatric exam. If one of these evaluations came up in the military, it might interfere with your promotion hearing. There's simply no way one would report such a sighting. The 777-pilot told me that he once saw a luminous swarm of light balls at 10,000 feet while approaching Albuquerque, NM airport. Another pilot approaching the airport also saw the glowing swarm. But neither of them made a report of it. There was simply no benefit to your career to talk about such things with your bosses back then.

For example, there was a sighting at Chicago O'Hare Airport in November 2006 over one of the gates operated by United.32 Many gate agents, pilots, and baggage handlers saw the large, grey, disc-like object hovering over the gate, and some took pictures. Two months later it made the nightly Chicago news. But United reminded all these employees within a short time via an internal memo not to talk about it. The FAA said it was a "weather phenomenon" despite witness reports of a solid disc-like object. Sound familiar?

There's a risk to those who talk about these topics of being marginalized, censored, or just seen as plain crazy. What's the downside? In the long run, our societies will become increasingly detached from reality, whether it's bigfoot or UFOs, as more people encounter these phenomena but have nowhere to go to talk about them.

However, on the other hand, if we can reframe these topics in the language of something that is at least remotely scientific and familiar, the stigma will be gone. We can start the conversation we should be having about these topics.

Chapter 3—Characteristics of Exposure to Coherent Matter

How do you know if you're in the presence of Coherent Matter? You'll start to see strange phenomena, especially concerning your electronic equipment and batteries. Other symptoms include effects on clocks, watches, and other fine-tuned instruments due to short-range but strong magnetic fields.

In 1969, NICAP (National Investigations Committee on Aerial Phenomena) published a book by Major Donald Keyhoe and Gordon Lore called "Strange Effects From UFOs."[33] The book lists case after case of strange phenomena around UFO sightings. Below is a summary of some of those unexplained effects and symptoms.

Consider just this one the case from Dale, Indiana, 1964. The witness reported a large, orange ball of light the size of a basketball land behind his house. Loose objects outside the home were pulled toward the luminous object, and the smell of sulfur was present. The thing then took off again.[34]

There are at least four symptoms that you are around Coherent Matter Phenomena. The first are orbs, balls of light, and luminosities. These are occasionally seen as ball lightning coming into a house, moving objects such as airplanes, or other things that alter the Earth's background electrostatic fields. Balls of light can sometimes be dangerous, even lethal, but often are harmless. They form a ball as the individual electrons have been compressed and have lost their unique identities; they have become "degenerate," as physics calls it, and instead are forming one big, charged particle: Thus, a ball of light. Nikola Tesla found these would show up in his labs.

Second, there will be strange electromagnetic effects. Batteries will fail, watches will stop, and car batteries will drain. We've seen these effects many times around crop circles, which I'll discuss in a subsequent chapter. But as the NICAP report makes clear, this is one of the fundamental characteristics of UFO encounters. And often cryptids, as well as we'll see in subsequent chapters.

Third, some soft x-rays or possibly harmful gamma radiation will be pumped out of the matter ball. These could be soft x-rays with a lower frequency or hard x-rays used in x-ray machines. If the system is pumped too far, there may also be dangerous gamma rays. That's why witnesses to these phenomena sometimes report being injured or burned.

Fourth, gravitational effects are seen in objects moving in a specific direction or floating. These are temporary effects that last for a few seconds to minutes. This accounts for things in a room seemingly hitting the ceiling for a few moments. This has also been reported around UFOs and cryptids.

The physicist John Archibald Wheeler, in a 1954 paper, tells us that tight clusters of subatomic particles will form a ring and create their own gravitational fields. He called these structures "Geons," which to my ear sounds like "gravitational ions" but actually stands for "gravitational electromagnetic entities."[35] They have no mass but possess an electromagnetic signature, i.e., possibly another type of dark matter.

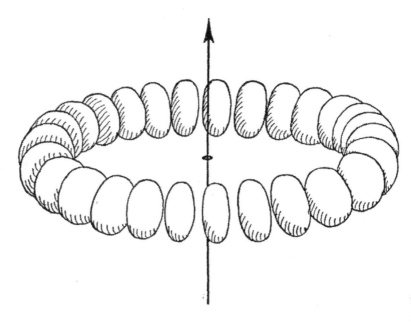

Fig. 11. John Wheeler's Geon (Gravitational Electromagnetic Entities)
(Image ©1955 from *Physical Review*)

This shows us how far back this research into Coherent Matter goes: at least 70 years and probably longer.

Here are some of the common effects that have been experienced around UFOs and other strange encounters.

Smell of Sulfur

Strange smells are often reported around paranormal phenomena, bigfoot, and UFO sightings. There are many examples of sulfur smells in the 1966 report by NICAP mentioned above, "Strange Effects From UFOs." Your mind can probably accept static and electrical odors around strange technologies, but what about bigfoot?

From a perspective of cold fusion/LENR it's known that these processes create nuclear transmutation of elements. Takaaki Matsumoto took photos of carbon films and sprays emerging from pure lead balls exposed to LENR experiments. In other cases, tungsten strips transmuted to pure carbon almost instantly. So, it is well known that cold fusion, through fusion and fission processes, creates new chemical elements on the spot. Matsumoto called it Electro Nuclear Regeneration. It's more commonly called alchemy which you and I were taught was fiction, and it turns out to be confirmed in the world of cold fusion/LENR.

Oxygen-16 is one of the most common elements on Earth, and its transmutation creates sulphur-32. This is a specific outcome of coherent matter creating an alchemical reaction. So the sulphuric odor and other rotten smells associated with these phenomena may result from elemental transmutation inherent in cold fusion.

Gravity Distortion

Another feature of coherent matter processes is the creation of gravitational changes at a microscopic level, specifically the creation of micro black holes at the center of charge clusters. This was confirmed by Winston H. Bostick, Ken Shoulders, Takaaki Matsumoto, John Wheeler and others. Ball lightning is often seen going against the direction of the wind, floating freely as if it's in its own gravitational frame of reference. That's because it's creating its own gravitational field due to Electro Nuclear Collapse created by John Wheeler's Geons. It's no accident that the US Air Force covertly funded Bostick and Wheeler's research in the 1950s. Even lab-produced ball lightning has its own gravitational fields.

In Vance Orchard's fascinating book *Bigfoot of the Blues*, all about sightings in the Walla Walla area and neighboring Blue Mountains, there are reports of gliding bigfoot.[36] This is like other reports where bigfoot gliding down or up to trees or from fence tops. Their movements don't seem weighty like ours would be if we were their size and stature. That's not to say that they don't make pounding booming sounds as they walk, as they sometimes do. But at other times, they don't seem to have the weight one would expect. And then there are the cases where their footprints end in the middle of trackable ground.

This last feature, abruptly ending footprints, is mentioned in *Hunt for the Skinwalker*, about strange sightings and encounters in the Uinta Basin, Utah. Kelleher and Knapp mention the oft-told account of a giant wolf-like creature that approached the owners of Skinwalker Ranch. Following its tracks, after it attacked one of the calves, experienced tracker and ranch owner Terry Sherman said they suddenly ended right next to other tracks 2-inches deep.[37] Perhaps this marks a phase change in the matter that constitutes these cryptids.

Battery and Camera Failure

This is an effect that I've seen many times around crop circles in the UK and US: the sudden failure of electronics, cameras, and batteries. I first noticed it big time in the 1999 Devil's Den formation at Fyfield Down, Wiltshire, UK. This is also seen around UFO sightings, bigfoot encounters, and

Fig. 12. Fyfield Down formation, 1999 (Photo by Author)

haunted locations. Below is a picture of the Fyfield Down "Devil's Den" formation of 1999, which caused multiple

Fig. 13. Batteries Instantly Drained at
Fyfield Down Crop Formation, 1999
(Photo by Author)

battery and camera failures (Figures 12 and 13). (See my video playlist for more: http://bitly.com/cropcircleweirdness)

This same effect has been seen in various episodes of the History Channel's "The Secret of Skinwalker Ranch" TV show. These researchers' batteries will just quit in unexpected ways.

From a coherent matter perspective, this effect is caused by the unbinding of charge clusters that can release a lot of voltage when they come apart from their unified state.

Sudden Cold

There will often be sudden cold in the vicinity of Coherent Matter. As mentioned above, this happens when the charge clusters come apart, and the individual particles assume their unique identities again, thus becoming incoherent. At this point, these objects will literally suck heat from their surroundings.

I once encountered a UFO witness at a store in White Plains, NY. He described being in Miami, Florida and walking over to a nearby 7-11 store from a friend's house. It was a warm summer night. When he came out of the store, suddenly, it was bone-chilling cold. He looked up and saw a sizeable luminous disc hovering over a nearby apartment building. And the next day, on his way to the airport, there was news of the event on a local radio station.

In the 1980s, journalist Brad Sorenson visited a secret area, possibly Lockheed Martin Skunkworks, near Edwards Air Force Base close to Palmdale, CA. This story was told to us by his friend, recently deceased graphics artist Mark McCandlish, who worked for

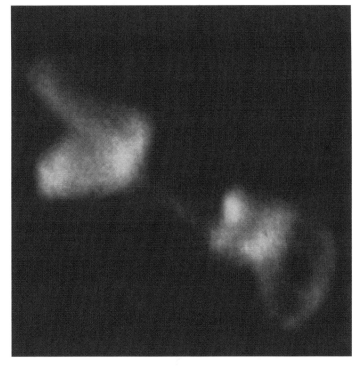

Fig. 14. Mobile Luminous Object at Hessdalen,
Norway
(Photo ©1982 by Project Hessdalen)

magazines like *Popular Mechanics*, creating concept art of secret black budget aircraft. Sorensen said that the area in the room around these three floating, disc-shaped craft was freezing.

Fig. 15. Mobile Luminous Object at Hessdalen,
Norway
(Photo ©1982 by Project Hessdalen)

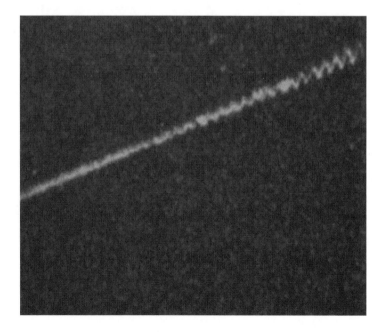

Fig. 16. Mobile Luminous Object at Hessdalen,
Norway
(Photo ©1984 by Project Hessdalen)

This type of experience is common to "paranormal" encounters from haunted locations to cryptids to UFOs. In Coherent Matter sciences, it is understood to be a result of charge clusters coming apart and renormalizing to their environment. The cold effect would be the cluster of electrons pulling in large amounts of heat from their local environment as the atoms become differentiated again.

The areas around bigfoot sightings are also known for the sudden cold effect. A witness in Yellowstone described the following experience. The witness was hiking the Continental Divide Trail, had just entered Yellowstone Park from the North, and was about ten miles from Old Faithful.

First, he encountered other hikers going the other way that told him that something weird was happening in the part of the park he was about to hike into. They wouldn't be more specific. A bit later, the hiker felt a telepathic voice telling him to go off the main trail. He then experienced something invisible pass him on the trail that made noise as it walked. Later that evening, he noticed something feeling around the bottom of his tent with its hand. Fleeing the tent, he hid in a tree nearby. Following strange howling sounds, he noticed it suddenly and inexplicably became cold even though it was mid-August.[38]

Some of the objects filmed by the Navy on the East and West coasts of the United States were also extremely cold, as seen by the dark appearance on the FLIR cameras, which sense heat. This would also suggest that whatever technology was powering these objects was pulling heat from the surrounding atmosphere.

Here's another relevant case. A police officer searching an abandoned house after its alarms went off noticed that a room on the second floor was freezing even though the rest of the second floor was over 100 degrees. There was nothing in the room to account for the cold and no air conditioning. After leaving, the alarm went off again, so the police returned. Even though they had shut the door when they left, the same room was now the same hot temperature as the rest of the house.[39]

This aspect of the phenomena was reported in the 1969 NICAP study. In 1954 a witness in Oregon City reported a feeling a sudden cold, like wind and rain drops on his skin and clothing, even though there was no wind or rain at the time, right before seeing a bright orange luminous object cross the sky in front of him. He then felt dizzy and light-headed, almost if he were about to float in the air.

Unexplained EMF Bursts

Cold fusion and LENR experiments are often accompanied by bursts of radio energy that can be picked up on an AM radio. Yes, ball lightning can be detected on an AM radio! According to Bychkov et al., it can be detected at frequencies of 300 kHz to 3 MHz. This excess EMF results from the charge clusters coming apart and releasing lots of energy in all parts of the electromagnetic spectrum. The same phenomena can sometimes be seen around UFO encounters and how they cause static in car radios. But overall, we're talking about what Alexander Parkhomov calls "Flicker Noise": where many interacting parts create non-linear, unexpected, and unpredictable outcomes.[40] (We'll discuss this idea again in a later chapter.)

Orbs

There is a big difference between glowing objects from ordinary plasmas and exotic vacuum objects. Plasmas are charged gases that can emit a lot of light and temporarily maintain a spherical shape. And they can be very hot. But they don't have the density of bunched electrons. They therefore lack any capacity for nuclear transmutation where new isotopes and elements will be produced. And usually, ball lightning is cool to the touch even though it's glowing. Therefore, plasmas and ball lightning are different phenomena with some overlap in appearance and physical properties: called "Plasmoids," magnetically shaped plasmas. They can appear around earthquakes, in areas of the Earth with lots of mineral deposits like quartz and copper, as in Hessdalen, Norway, and thunderstorms.[41]

In their books, Where the Footprints End: Volumes I and II, Cutchin and Renner present many cases of light orbs seen around bigfoot, in some cases, the creatures holding or even hurling balls of light at witnesses.[42] Witnesses such as Kenny Collins have also reported seeing bigfoot emerging from balls of light.[43]

Les Stroud on the *Survivorman Bigfoot* show mentioned seeing balls of light at a site near Portland, OR, and also hearing telepathic voices in his head. He even visited a psychologist later to ensure he wasn't going   nuts.[44]

Ron Morehead also reported balls of light near where bigfoot had been heard many times at the famed Sierra Camp, high in the Sierra Nevada Mountains of California. He also reported hearing a tuning fork-type sound over the camp structure one night. Another time he saw what appeared to be a luminous sword, like a light saber moving between nearby trees.

Micro Sparks

Takaaki Matsumoto noticed in his Cold Fusion lab experiments tiny ball lightnings that were on the surface of his materials that then lifted off and exploded.[45] This has been seen around some bigfoot sightings as in this case from Yellowstone National Park, where a woman and her friend were dipping in a natural hot spring that is open for bathing part of the year. According to the witness, blue sparks were coming off the creature, their car wouldn't start as it approached, and their car's battery returned to life as the creature moved away.[46]

Cold Electricity and Radiant Energy

This type of energy is where electricity is made not by typical charge separation like in batteries and AC circuits but by converting thermal energy into an electrical flow. Tesla called this "radiant energy" because it acts like light. It is blocked by wood and metal surfaces. Still, it can be felt in your body as an intense tingling sensation, something I've experienced during a PK (psychokinesis) demonstration in Japan. The PK practitioner ran his hand above my arm, a few inches away, and it felt like electric pins and needles inside my arm, not just on the surface.

Time Loss

Witnesses also report time loss that is associated with orbs and ball lightning. Consider the following case: A registered nurse took a nighttime walk in Holly, Michigan, in 2018. A couple was walking ahead of her on the bridge. She remembers an orb 2 ft. high came from her right side and moved along the bridge. The next thing she knew, it was 3 AM, there was no couple on the bridge anymore, and she had no explanation for the time lost. (*Canam Missing* YouTube channel, April 2022)

Miniature Black Holes

Dr. Alexander Parkhomov, in his groundbreaking book *SPACE. EARTH. HUMAN.*, mentions several sudden anomalous gravitational effects from incidents in Russia that he attributes to small black holes entering the Earth's atmosphere.[47] Such hypothetical tiny black holes are also seen in cold fusion experiments. They will be expected to be produced by biological sources of charge clusters if cryptids are capable of this. Therefore, we would expect cryptid encounters to yield weird gravitational anomalies.

Such an event was reported by Russian researcher Dr. Igor Burtsev. He said that one such encounter led to various-sized objects levitating in his van and the engine starting by itself even though no battery was connected at that moment. In personal communications with him, he said that not only small objects levitated in the creature's presence but also a footstool, a 20-liter can of water, and a light bulb coming out of its ceiling socket. He also said that a 5-ruble coin flew across a bed and fell on the pillow next to his head.[48]

Takaaki Matsumoto argues that cold fusion reactions frequently create tiny black holes.[49] These gravitationally intense but short-lived particles do not escape their immediate environment but can create locally strong attractive forces. So imagine that mini black holes could be right around you the next time you experience something "paranormal."

Looking over the literature and experiences of people around paranormal phenomena, we find these same strange characteristics over and over. While they may represent principles we don't know about, it's equally plausible that they are the effects of coherent matter phenomena in different forms. They could be symptoms of lifeforms built around this type of matter.

UFOs and Sasquatch Appearing in the Same Areas

This is some of the most substantial evidence that we're dealing with coherent matter phenomena: you know how the old saying goes, "friends of a feather flock together."

Why would we see apparently incongruent phenomena together, like a big, hairy ape-man and the epitome of high tech, a UFO? They're both products of similar natural processes where matter can shift states from solid to plasmas to coherency. It wouldn't be surprising that such entities in our universe, or multiverse, can associate with each other.

Stan Gordon's book, *Silent Invasion,* about UFO and Bigfoot sightings in Pennsylvania in the early 1970s, chronicles how frequently these two phenomena are seen together. Gordon lists sighting after sighting of UFO and bigfoot-type creatures, one after the other, throughout the same geographical areas. Sometimes both were seen at the same time.

Kewaunee Lapseritis presented similar information at the *Open Minds UFO Congress* at Fountain Hills, Arizona, in 2014. He said he had studied cases from Great Falls, Montana, in 1976 where Sasquatch were seen in UFOs' vicinity. The reader is probably also that this area is the center of numerous ICBM launch facilities where missiles have been tampered with and disabled by UFOs starting in the 1960s.

Similarly, Kelleher and Knapp also mention a case from Elbert County, CO where a series of strange occurrences on a ranch culminated in the rancher encountering two ET-like beings with big heads and eyes and a flying saucer nearby but also a bigfoot next to the saucer. This suggests that these objects and entities share a similar frequency and reality that sometimes overlaps with ours.

Overlapping Realities

Coherent matter has different characteristics than the ordinary electrostatic matter that we're used to, where gravity holds things down and solid objects have distinct boundaries. So this whole discussion may seem kind of strange to you, even weird and unbelievable. Yet, I'm confident that coherent matter is equally as real as the other types of matter that we're used to.

From our perspective, it would appear as overlapping realities with all sorts of strange effects that we usually call "paranormal." But as UFO researcher, disclosure advocate, and former Dept. of Defense official Lue Elizondo often points out, the prefix "para" just means "next to." Like the words "paramedic" or "parachute." So "paranormal" simply means other phenomena next to our reality, not necessarily anything inherently strange.

Coherent matter systems and charge clusters are constantly making and breaking chemical elements. They are not static. So ordinary matter would experience "breaking," and then the coherent matter would be "making" new chemicals and processes. (Watch the *Martin Fleischmann Memorial Project* YouTube channel to learn more.) And we could expect this principle to equally apply to our interaction with UFOs and cryptids.

Chapter 4—Why Did a Secret DIA Program Study Strange Phenomena at Skinwalker Ranch?

"For eight years, a team of highly trained scientists and others came face-to-face with a terrifying reality that, on superficial examination, appeared to break the laws of science but that, in fact, was consistent with modern-day physics."[51] — Kelleher, Colm and George Knapp

"Some of the security guards out there were trained, battle-hardened individuals, but what they encountered at Skinwalker Ranch scared and shook them up deeply."[52] —Dr. John Alexander, US Army Colonel (retired)

One of the first recent indications of the US government's interest in and study of anomalous phenomena came in the *New York Times* and *Politico* 2017 articles about the Pentagon's UFO program called AATIP (Advanced Aerospace Threat Identification Program). The article mentioned former Pentagon deputy assistant director for intelligence Chris Mellon as a massive proponent of UFO disclosure.

Shortly after the *Times* article appeared, some of Mellon's presentation slides, including "slide 9," prepared for a classified congressional presentation about AATIP, were leaked on the internet. The slide listed several exotic psycho-energetic effects that anomalous objects and UAPs can have on people and machines including "penetration of solid surfaces," "psychophysiological effect," "instantaneous sensory disassembly," "unique cognitive human interfaces," and "anomalies in space/time construct".[53]

For many researchers, this slide revealed what they had suspected for a long time: a concern amongst DoD officials about incursions into US air space of anomalous phenomena with attendant weird biological and physical effects. Slide 9 also mentioned DoD "having properties where such phenomena can be studied."

The Mellon slide was referring to the Skinwalker Ranch, among other properties. Kelleher and Knapp mentioned such places in their book, such as Dulce, New Mexico, an area on the East side of the Cascade Mountains in Washington State, and a ranch in Elbert County, Colorado. If you're wondering how the Pentagon's primary intelligence agency came to be studying cryptids, orbs, and UFOs at a remote location in Northern Utah, you're not alone. How could a military defense agency even have an interest or jurisdiction to investigate a remote ranch within the United States for paranormal activity?

Well, the answer, according to 25-year veteran CIA officer John Ramirez, in an interview with The Black Vault's John Greenwald, is that there is an office within DIA that investigates and monitors what is called MASINT: Measure and Signatures Intelligence. Basically, the whole electromagnetic spectrum as we know it. The MASINT folks at DIA, specifically the DIA D/T department, look for abnormal electromagnetic signatures within the United States as part of the general defense of the country. And you know what that means: they're most likely picking signals from UFOs, UAPs, AAVs (Anomalous Aerial Vehicles), and similar phenomena. And anything else anomalous out there they can pick up. So if DIA analysts are out there at Skinwalker Ranch or Dulce, NM, or anywhere else where unexplained activity happens repeatedly, there are frequencies that can be picked up at that location. (Watch the Ramirez Interview: https://youtu.be/eXerKPm2-p4)

The recent UFO/UAP incidents we've heard about, like the USS Nimitz naval incidents in 2004, USS Roosevelt in 2015, and others like 2021 USS Kearsarge encounters, were not the beginning of the government's interest in these topics, just the ones that have become public.

One of those programs was the AAWSAP program (Advanced Aerial Weapons Systems Application Program) started in 2008 through the efforts of Senator Harry Reid and other senators. According to Lacatski et al., the AAWSAP program was a UFO research program disguised as something more mundane, hence the long bureaucratic-sounding acronym. They also tell us that AATIP was simply a convenient nickname for AAWSAP and Skinwalker Ranch was a very big part of the study program. According to *New York Post* reporter Stephen Greenstreet, the Skinwalker research program consumed a whopping 97 percent of AAWSAP funding.[54]

Science advisor to the program Dr. Hal Puthoff, solicited 38 research papers from respective experts. And, as he told us at a meeting in Las Vegas in 2018, even these experts didn't know the goals of the program. The purpose of the papers was to see if any of the phenomena surrounding UFOs or the activities at Skinwalker were comprehensible to any scientists with the best knowledge available. Or was all of this beyond what even the most advanced science of the day could comprehend? Puthoff and crew concluded none of the UFO or Skinwalker activity they were studying, including the Nimitz incidents of 2004, could easily fit within the bounds of existing scientific knowledge.

Pentagon Interest in Shapeshifting Skinwalkers

Until recently, the public didn't know much about the activities of AAWSAP, as even Hal Puthoff could only tell us so much in 2018. However, the recent book, *Skinwalkers at the Pentagon*, published in 2021 and cleared by the Pentagon after a 14-month review, details some of the activities of the Pentagon's AAWSAP program and the role of the Bigelow Aerospace Advanced Space Studies (BAASS) program in investigating strange phenomena at the infamous Skinwalker Ranch. Skinwalker is located in the Uinta Basin in Northern Utah, which is known as a "hotspot" for UFOs, bigfoot, cryptids, and other strange encounters.

Weird phenomena like hovering dark masses, cryptid animals like a mysterious "Dino-Beaver," something like a cross between a three-hundred-pound Stegosaurus dinosaur and a beaver, and balls of light are mentioned in the book. And in some instances, we're told that researchers experienced these same anomalies at home upon return from the ranch. These included the seven-foot-tall wolf-like animals on two legs known as dogman, orbs, other strange activities including dark humanoid forms in their homes, and a huge owl-type creature that attacked one researcher's car.

Looking at some of these strange phenomena, we see their characteristics also match that of coherent matter, including cold spots, luminosities, and unexplained radiation injuries. The History Channel show about the ranch, now in its third season, has shown viewers some of these strange subjects.

I don't think this is a coincidence. These incidents are exactly what you would expect from exposure to coherent matter phenomena. For example, it's well known from research in Low Energy Nuclear Reaction that when charge clusters explode or come apart, they "dishevel," as researcher Robert Greenyer refers to it. They suck heat from their environment and instantly make that area cold. How many times have you heard this happening around haunted and ghost encounters, not to mention bigfoot? It seems like we're dealing with the same thing, whether in the lab or in the field: super-rapid temperature fluctuations that consume heat, an "endothermic" reaction.

Health Effects of Contact with Condensed Matter

One of the cases studied by BAASS researchers mentioned in Skinwalkers at the Pentagon is where a blue ball of light allegedly went through a witness while in the car with his daughter somewhere in the North-West of the US. The daughter said she saw the balls of light come across from a field on the left side of the car and pass through her father's chest and right shoulder in the car. The father subsequently suffered some health effects and burns from this incident.

This looks similar to an injury that Italian researcher Francesco Piantelli received from an experimental cold fusion reactor. After starting up the device, an orb was emitted on the outside of the reactor and caused a severe burn to his shoulder. So this type of technology needs to be used with caution and not driven to extremes.

Gamma radiation is also a result of natural and artificial radioactive decay and nuclear fusion. Balls of light that emit such radiation would likely produce it due to highly energized electrons that exist in charge clusters and Exotic Vacuum Objects, as Kenneth Shoulders called them. Whether balls of light that inflict such damage are entirely natural objects or controlled by some higher intelligence remains to be seen. But the main point is that ball lightning can be dangerous or even lethal, especially if they explode, even if they don't create any heat whatsoever.

A witness in Philadelphia, Joe, described precisely this happening to him one day while digging a drainage ditch near a house:

> I was digging a ditch for rainwater off the roof to go to the swell between houses, and a storm came and went. I could

hear the thunder about 2 miles away in Chestnut Hill. I live in a Valley nearby. I was hosing the patio because I had muddy feet from digging, putting the hose down, I was on the balls of my feet, and out of the corner of my eye I saw a orange/red ball above one of the holes (about 3 feet round) and all of a sudden a boom: I went flying about 8 to 10 feet. I was looking up at the sky, thinking I was dead.[55]

Other possibilities include cymatic effects, waves of reinforcing and cancelling sound, that could be driven by a highly resonant ball of light. These sound waves, if intense enough, could cause biological damage to human tissue and even DNA material if they were strong enough.

In another instance, according to Lacatski et al., a group of three DIA scientists were walking on a trail and encountered a dark, amorphous shape that they could only see on their night vision scope. It had intense cold air around it. Approaching the shape, they all felt an increasing feeling of heightened fear. They could get no closer than 50 yards to the object, "each one convinced that continuing towards the dark oval shape would lead to certain death".[56] I could be wrong here, but that sounds a lot like the "plasma stealth" mentioned by John Ramirez or "black ball lightning" in a recent scientific article.[57] Invisible black ball lightning was also mentioned extensively in the 1994 Fryberger paper from the Stanford Linear Accelerator Center.

If you've ever read any books by John Keel, such as *The Mothman Prophecies*, one of the first books I ever came across in this genre as a teenager, he also mentioned venturing into "zones of fear" when investigating cryptids in West Virginia. So, I'm going to assume we're dealing with the same thing here, be it at Skinwalker Ranch or Mothman territory back in West Virginia.

Ron Morehead, in his *Voices in Wilderness* book, describing decades of contact with bigfoot in the Sierra Nevada mountains of California, mentioned something similar. He said he and a colleague were walking towards the source of the "reverse samurai" chattering language they heard so much at their forest camp.[58] At one point, they felt like they were within 15 feet of the source of the vocalizations, yet nothing was visible, and they could physically go no farther toward it. It was like there was an invisible wall in front of them.

On another occasion, as mentioned above, Lacatski et al. say that two Defense Intelligence Agency researchers saw what looked like a dinosaur-like creature the size of a gigantic pig but with stegosaurus-like spines on its back and a paddle-like tail like what a beaver would have. The researchers followed it around the corner of a building, where it vanished in thin air. Lacatski   continues:

> Metallic UAPs, flying orbs of varying colors, otherworldly creatures, discarnate voices, poltergeist, electromagnetic anomalies, and orange "portals" have co-located as well as materialized separately on the property. These extraordinary phenomena have been witnessed by scores of independent visitors to the ranch almost continuously between 1994 and 2021.[59]

Many of these phenomena share similarities to those produced by gravitational collapse and intense electromagnetic compression that Matsumoto talked about in his 1992 paper on cold fusion. Intense magnetic fields created by condensed matter create new types of matter, gravitational fields, and electromagnetic states. In other words, I believe we're talking about the same phenomena as Lacatski and his fellow researchers. Lifeforms with advanced abilities compared to humans in terms of energy utilization, cloaking, and teleportation. No wonder the Pentagon considered the area a possible security threat worthy of an in-depth study.

"The Other Topic"

Lacatski isn't the only intelligence official to come forward recently to talk about orbs, UFOs, and "hard-to-explain phenomena." John Ramirez mentioned above tells us that he was aware of two highly classified programs, UFOs and glowing orbs, which he referred to as "balls of energy." He said these orbs were detected by KH-11 spy satellites that monitored Soviet and later Russian missile launches. These orbs would show up around these missiles and exhibit a "stealth plasma" invisible mode where they are only visible in the infra-red spectrum. There was even an unofficial online group of CIA officers who discussed the non-classified aspects of this "other topic" on a bulletin board in the early days of the internet. Topics also included UFOs, extraterrestrials, and related subjects, which current Director of National Intelligence Avril Haines referred to as the "other topic." People in the intelligence community have been interested in a wide gamut of "paranormal topics" for a long time: the real X-Files.

Ramirez went on to say that a highly classified "Orb Working Group" formed around the same time as AAWSAP. These orbs were originally of interest to the DIA and CIA due to observations of domes of light appearing near Soviet missile testing sites caused by orbs flying in from high over the Arctic regions. These were the same orbs flying around US nuclear missile installations and facilities and present in the USSR.

And perhaps, most importantly, Ramirez tells us that these orbs of light are the energetic aspect of physical UFOs, of "the phenomenon." These orbs are, according to him, the same phenomena as UFOs.

Now I'm not saying that my perspective here, that coherent matter, explains every aspect of the Skinwalker phenomenon. But there's definite overlap and consistency with what we've seen in other fields of science, so much so that we can find many ways that they seem like the same thing.

It's also evident that high levels of classification within the US government on this subject have prevented any intelligent level of public discussion about it. And here we have to figure it out for ourselves, you and me, with only the slightest degree of thoughtful dialogue from the agencies that know something about it.

So now that our federal government has all but told us that cryptids, UFOs, orbs, and other things are all part of "the phenomenon," where does that leave us? To me, they're giving us the green light to go ahead and research these topics, investigate the data, and decide what it all means. Without actually saying to the general public, "unidentifiable entities and monsters are just outside your door, maybe even in your house. They're real."

Midwestern Town Suffers Electromagnetic Collapse

We've seen in this chapter how the Pentagon, Defense Intelligence Agency, and Central Intelligence Agency have had long-standing interests in UFOs, UAP, and related phenomena through deeply classified programs like the ones John Ramirez mentioned. Hal Puthoff said similar things at his 2018 SSE/IRVA meeting presentation: the government continued to study UFOs after Project Bluebook ended. It just did so secretly. AAWSAP and AATIP are just some of the recent programs we know.

Several years ago, I had the opportunity to talk with a former Dept. of Defense official over dinner at a remote viewing conference in Las Vegas. He mentioned to me the following curious incident.

Apparently, using some observational system that remains classified today, the US government sometime in the 1960s saw that a small town in the Midwest of the US had utterly lost all types of electrical function. This condition, which lasted for about a day, affected power lines, batteries, cars, and all battery-operated devices like wristwatches. In other words, a complete collapse of some portion of the electromagnetic spectrum. When I asked him what had caused this condition, he said they didn't know. He also refused to tell me how the government had detected this abnormal condition affecting the town. I suspect it has something to do with the MASINT program, mentioned by retired intelligence officer John Ramirez, which constantly scans the US for strange electromagnetic activity.

I believe this weird event establishes the similarity of these phenomena, as I've presented it so far in the previous chapters. I've experienced something similar around crop circles, like bigfoot witnesses and many who have encountered close-up UFOs. Abnormal electrical conditions are a hallmark of coherent matter systems in any shape.

So let's look a little more at how prevalent cold fusion reactions are in the everyday world that we're familiar with. And how these same scientific principles that underly cold fusion have been studied and researched worldwide for decades.

Chapter 5—The Prevalence of Cold Fusion and Its Importance to Life on Earth

"Cold Fusion reactions seem to easily take place everywhere."[60]
— Takaaki Matsumoto

We've discussed in the previous chapters how stigma and ridicule exist against new scientific discoveries that challenge existing belief systems. This condition doesn't only apply to UFO and bigfoot witnesses. It applies to any radically new scientific discovery that could render an older paradigm obsolete: Especially the subject of so-called "cold fusion."

In 1989 Martin Fleischmann and Stanley Pons of the University of Utah, Salt Lake, held a press conference to announce the findings of their cold fusion research: a process that created excess heat with deuterium (heavy water) or ordinary water and palladium rods. They weren't the first to experiment with this process but became the most publicized in recent times. It wasn't their idea to hold a controversial press conference; they would have preferred to keep researching the subject for several more years without any outside scrutiny. However, their bosses at the university wanted to have a "prior claim" on the technology so they could file for a patent. Hundreds of labs attempted to reproduce their results, but few did. And as a result, Fleischmann and Pons were seriously ridiculed, and mainstream science labeled cold fusion as "junk science." Scientists at MIT held a "mock wake" for cold fusion, denouncing it as "deceased." President Bush senior formed a presidential commission was to determine if cold fusion was confirmed or not, with the help of hot fusion researchers at MIT. And subsequently, the US Patent Office refused to give patents in the subject area. Officially, the subject was now dead.

Many attempted to recreate the Fleischmann/Pons results and failed. At the same time, other well-qualified researchers worldwide understood the Fleischmann/Pons reaction and successfully reproduced it. One of those was Takaaki Matsumoto, a Japanese nuclear scientist at the Sapporo University, Hokkaido. Matsumoto correctly identified why other labs hadn't replicated the Fleischmann/Pons results: they had used the wrong type of palladium and had a mistaken idea of how it worked. The reaction didn't take place on the palladium surface: it took place in the cracks. And strange effects were produced beyond excess heat once all those hydrogen atoms clustered in the palladium cracks. Matsumoto called these gravitational effects "Electro-Nuclear Collapse": a state where electromagnetic pressure in condensed matter becomes so intense that it tears atoms apart and reconstitutes them in new ways.

Matsumoto's extensive writings on the subject showed that he had penetrated the mystery of cold fusion. Yet the world had never heard of Matsumoto outside of a small circle of cold fusion researchers because Fusion Technology Magazine had banned him from publishing in their magazine in 1996. His previous articles from 1989 and 1990 appeared in the Fusion Technology, but then the editors changed their minds on the subject and decided to ban his publications.

Takaaki Matsumoto and the Nattoh Model

Matsumoto carefully explained the cold fusion work of Fleischmann and Pons as the effect of resonating hydrogen clusters. When the clusters become densely packed to a sufficient degree, they undergo Electro-Nuclear Collapse, an intense micro-gravitational effect, and lose their identity. They become like primordial matter that can transmute even radioactive matter to harmless materials such as carbon and silver. Because of the mesh-like structure of these hydrogen clusters, he called it the "Nattoh Model," after the fermented soybean dish so popular in Japan. Nattoh looks like little lumps of soybeans connected by a congealed, jellylike mass.

Matsumoto was not the only one to support Fleischmann and Pons. Ken Shoulders, a colleague of Hal Puthoff's at Stanford Research Institute, also worked on the issue of charge clusters for many years. To explain the work of Canadian researcher John Hutchison and his astounding fractured metal samples created with replicated Nikola Tesla technology, Shoulders finally came up with a more specific name for his "strong electron charge clusters." He simply called them Exotic Vacuum Objects: Dense clusters of electrons that could bury themselves in metal, feed on other electrons, and self-sustain themselves and their shape, what physicists call solitons, for long periods.

And even before Matsumoto and Shoulders was the work of George Mesyats in Russia, who had discovered the same phenomena of charge clusters and called them "Ectons," short for "explosive electron clusters." Working in isolation in Russia, Mesyats wasn't aware that anyone else had already observed the same thing. And another person who preceded Matsumoto was Yule Brown in the 1980s, who had also noticed compressed matter's transformational, alchemical effects.

However, Matsumoto was one of the first to grasp the universality of the cold fusion process, how widespread it is in our universe, even powering the activity of stars:

> Since the hydrogen cluster can contain many hydrogens, possibly many millions, many strange reactions are associated with the primary reactions: productions of heavy elements and multiple-neutron nuclei, formations of tiny black holes, and so on. *Readers will easily understand that cold fusion is a small-scale simulation of the events that occur in cold stars far away in the universe.*[61] (My emphasis)

Essentially, Matsumoto is saying that cold fusion is one of the most fundamental processes found in the universe.

A universal process found in all types of matter, including stars, planets, and living organisms. The process of gravitational collapse is already seen in Neutron Stars, and Matsumoto claims that the same process happens at an atomic level in some types of condensed matter. He suggests that the shift to understanding cold fusion as a microcosm of how stars work is the same as the shift from Ptolemaic thinking to the Copernican worldview 500 years ago. While the Ptolemaic view correctly predicted planetary motion in our solar system, it did so with excessive complexity requiring unique orbital motions like epicycles, deferents, eccentrics, and equants.[63] And those extra motions didn't actually exist: they appeared to exist only from our perspective of other planets seen from Earth. The Copernican view greatly simplified our understanding of the cosmos and paved the way for a new worldview where the Earth was no longer the center of everything.

And the new simplicity of Copernican thinking paved the way for Giordano Bruno to propose the idea that faraway stars were simply other suns like ours. Those stars probably also had other planets like Earth. And these distant planets might have animals and life, similar and different from ours. And hence, the universe was infinite. Some cosmologists have encapsulated this latter idea in the idea of "eternal inflation": a Big Bang that never ceases to expand.

Similarly with cold fusion, if it's a fundamental process that occurs not only in deuterium atom lab experiments but also in all types of hydrogen atoms, the most abundant chemical in the universe, it creates a continuity of phenomena from the atomic scale to the cosmic. This "fractal universe" model allows us to see things in a new way and permits new ideas to exist in our minds and social belief systems. I'm not trying to convince you that this is the only approach to cold fusion. Still, it is a reasonable scientific possibility with lots of empirical evidence and learn more about it here in Chapter 12.

Matsumoto is telling us that the same forces that create black holes far in the other galaxies also exist within the atomic realm. And it is this type of "gravitational decay" or collapse that powers cold fusion, and it takes place at all scales in the universe, from galaxies to cells:

> It seems difficult to accept that the black hole can be generated in the cell because it is usually considered that the black hole in the universe needs a mass 10 times over than that of the sun. The fact is contrary. Since the gravitational force is employed to compress and completely destroy an assembly of neutrons, an extremely heavy mass is required. The gravitational force is the weakest among four naturally existing forces. However, if the electromagnetic force is effectively employed, it is easier to generate a tiny black hole, since the electromagnetic force is about 40 orders stronger than the gravitational force.[64]

And thus, electromagnetic forces generate tiny black holes at the cellular level compressing atoms and their neutrons into new types of materials.

The intense pressures of hydrogen clusters found everywhere in the universe and ordinary water are what powers these transformations. And so anything with water can create cold fusion, including plants, animals, and cells.

Ken Shoulders makes a similar point:

> There is a good chance common, small-sized EVOs can be classified as legitimate black holes; although I am sure Astronomers will object to this . . . Such associations lower the status of astronomy by being compared to mundane and ubiquitous examples. Still, when making a comparison between common, everyday EVOs, even obtained by sparking to a doorknob, the resemblance in a fundamental sense is striking.[65]

Again, we come back to the central point: that we're dealing with the same fundamental natural principles here, be it in spirals, galaxies, or water running down your bathtub drain. Specific shapes and patterns generate exotic energetic states that biological lifeforms can harness. The fact that modern humans haven't completely figured this out doesn't mean other lifeforms don't already incorporate these principles in their physiology.

The Structure of Cold Fusion

Matsumoto was one of the first to understand and explain how the cold fusion process works. The original idea was that it was similar to Hot Fusion in the neutrons of hydrogen were fusing and releasing heat in the process. But through careful observation of laboratory experiments, Matsumoto had figured out by 1989 that cold fusion reactions are actually driven by tightly meshed hydrogen clusters that compress the neutrons in the hydrogen atom. This compression leads to the emission of neutrinos (along with positrons and electrons) to form more clusters: a chain reaction. Matsumoto calls such structures "itonic clusters." These densely packed structures are the source of excess heat in cold fusion, not neutrons that are fusing.

A common objection to cold fusion is that the Coulombic Barrier, an electrostatic repulsive force that keeps subatomic particles from interacting, would prevent such fusion from happening. But neutrinos are not subject Coulombic Repulsion as they are tiny compared to neutrons. So that objection disappears, making cold fusion all the more plausible. David Fryberger of the Stanford Linear Accelerator Center Research makes a similar point in his ball lightning study published in 1994.

Matsumoto realized that cold fusion reactions occur not in a lattice, such as the even and ordered structure of atoms within a crystal, but on the surface or cracks of solids. In other words, you don't need perfectly manufactured substances to create cold fusion: it can happen in natural materials made of mixed elements and imperfect structures, just like we find in nature.

Researcher Winston H. Bostick found the same thing in the 1950s doing research funded by the US Air Force, into how to turn nuclear fusion reactions found in hydrogen bombs into helpful energy for peaceful purposes. He proposed that the same energetic plasmas he could generate in test tubes were not only the same shape as galaxies but also held together by the same electromagnetic processes. In fact, energy vortices interact at all scales, whether at atomic or galactic scales.

And Michael Solin, in his 1992 patent, described the same phenomena: coherent matter waves at an atomic level similar to what happens in stars:

A superconducting nuclear condensate is a magnetic liquid metal nuclear fuel that *generates energy with the generation of coherent radiation* under conditions of nuclear phase transformations in the mass of the initial product and the combination of electromagnetic, gravitational and nuclear interactions in it.[66] (my emphasis)

Matsumoto, Solin, and Bostick are all making the same claim: that self-organized, compressed, coherent types of matter can generate new states of energy with superconducting states, excess heat, and nuclear transmutation.

In essence, it appears that ball lightning, far from being an exotic, rare phenomenon, is one of the primary building blocks of nature!

And this process creates all the heavy elements we find on Earth (oxygen, silicon, nitrogen, for example). Natural fusion processes produce those elements within the Earth itself, not just from stellar processes millions of years ago, as we have been told.

Connection of Micro Ball Lightning to Earthquakes

Matsumoto also showed a connection between Japanese earthquakes and fireballs' appearance around the exact locations and time due to rock compression. These mysterious light phenomena are clusters of particles produced by extreme pressure, whether it's in the Earth's crust or a laboratory setting.

In Matsumoto's view, ball lightning is easily produced anywhere these conditions exist and through ultrasonic vibration and cavitation, heating, compression, fission, and laser and electron beams.[67]

I think you can see what this means. It's crucial: Matsumoto is telling us that charge clusters, ball lightning, and the like are the norm in nature, not the exception. If it's hard for us to understand, that shows us how far we are from understanding how nature works. And he found that these clusters could grow to over 3 feet in length.

Matsumoto discovered a wide range of effects related to cold fusion, some of which Martin Fleischmann had also studied. For example, Matsumoto noticed a helicity, a spinning motion, in the charge clusters he observed; he called them "energetic rotational waves." There was a new type of radiation not created by particle decay but by the pressure put on the neutrons by a mesh-like electron structure: this *strange radiation* was also discovered by Russian researcher Alexander Shishkin. In addition to this new type of radiation, there are soft x-rays, UV emissions, and EM pulses. Matsumoto also noticed gravity decay within these electron clusters, even a kind of electricity that was "cold." And also, that ball lightning had a tiny counterpart he dubbed "micro ball lightning" or MBL. Matsumoto noticed these micro ball lightnings from carefully examining his cold fusion reactions in his lab. Finally, micro sparks were seen on the surface of the nuclear reactions and other "strange particles and waves."

So basically, it would seem like almost every weird thing seen around paranormal activity is also seen on a small scale in cold fusion reactions. I don't think that is a coincidence, and it's more likely they're the same thing.

Matsumoto and Shishkin weren't the first to notice a new type of radiation. Charles G. Barkla, Nobel Prize winner in 1930 for the discovery of x-rays, also claimed that there was another type of radiation he called "J-radiation." Even with several decades of study, he could never explain it because it is not emitted by electrons or the ordinary decay of the atomic nucleus. So research into mysterious energies did not originate with cold fusion experiments but goes back over 100 years.

The critical takeaway from Matsumoto is that cold fusion works like a chain reaction, continuously producing excess heat because the electron clusters get energy from the relic neutrinos coming in from space (and the quantum vacuum). Cold fusion is, in essence, powered by dark matter.

And not only that, but Matsumoto argues that cold fusion reactions produce more dark matter as the chain reaction continues. Parkhomov's research, mentioned earlier, supports a similar conclusion: Relic neutrinos go in, and, through a process known in physics as "inverse beta-decay," cold neutrinos go out. And those neutrinos that come out are monochromatic, meaning all at the same temperature and frequency. Dark matter isn't just something way out there in space; it's powering every biological and chemical reaction we know. And it appears our friends, the cryptids, can tap into this chain reaction and get energy from it. Something we lowly humans haven't figured out how to do consciously yet.

Project Poltergeist

The initial attempt to detect neutrinos was made with existing nuclear reactors. In the Cowan-Reines experiment in 1956 at Oak Ridge, called Project Poltergeist, researchers set up two huge water tanks to detect these "ghostly," tiny neutrinos. Even then, a Nobel Prize wasn't awarded to the experimenters for the discovery until 1995! This is how long it takes to accept new ideas and discoveries, no wonder the concept of superconducting bigfoot isn't widely accepted yet:)

Relic Neutrinos—Unsung Heroes of Paranormal Worlds

Relic neutrinos have a comparatively large frequency, what scientists call the "de Broglie Wavelength," from around 4 mm more or less to as occasionally as large as 1 meter.

Because of this enormous "neutrino cross section," it is more likely to interact with matter than a solar neutrino. The de Broglie Wavelength isn't a literal frequency like your AM or FM radio; it's a quantum measurement that tells us about the probability density of finding the particle in a particle area. As the DB wavelength is generally around 4 mm, about 1/6th of an inch, it's most likely to be found in a place that can interact with biological material. In essence, the relic neutrino happens to be tuned to interact with our bodies and other natural objects of the same magnitude. In short, nature has designed a particle, which has existed since the Big Bang, that can interact with biological entities in a quantum way. Unlike the other type of neutrinos that constantly stream through our bodies, emanating from the sun but only rarely interacting with us, these relic neutrinos are comparatively massive. So they're interacting with biological systems and physical matter.

This "interaction potential" is significant because for the longest time, since the birth of Quantum Mechanics, we've been told that quantum interactions are for microscopic systems only. There is no impact on macroscopic-sized objects like us. From this viewpoint, large things like biological entities, cells, and so forth are governed by the same Newtonian mechanics that describe planetary orbits and satellites in the sky. Now we can see a class of quantum objects in the mesoscopic range that interact with macroscopic-scale atoms and cells in our reality. That's a considerable size for a subatomic particle.

Relic neutrinos are what physicists call a fermion as opposed to bosons that naturally form pairs. On the other hand, fermions are solitary particles, but they can create a condensate. And everyone agrees that relic neutrinos have a non-zero rest mass which means clumps of them can add up to something big that interacts with matter. And they're densely packed enough to be just about everywhere you find gravitationally significant objects like Earth. Relic neutrino particles are estimated to be about 1.5 mm away from each other on average, meaning their wavelength of 4 to 5 mm overlaps with their particle distance. These particles are naturally entangled because they were all created simultaneously after the Big Bang. Hence, "spooky action at a distance" comes into play. They are also non-relativistic, i.e., slow compared to the speed of light, about 1000-10,000km per second, a tiny fraction of light's speed of 300km per second.

So, they're relatively big, slow, and interactive and about a million times bigger than the better-known solar neutrino, which only rarely interacts with anything.

Decoupling in Early Universe

Scientists tell us that these relic neutrinos decoupled themselves from the rest of the particles in the universe about 1 or 2 seconds after the Big Bang. In essence, these abundant energetic particles are independent of other energy sources in the universe and operate on their own frequency. In short, relic neutrinos are doing their own thing!

The neat part in all of this is that relic neutrinos have an earthly counterpart: Cold Neutrinos (also called Slow Neutrinos). They arise in high temperatures and nuclear reactions like cold fusion. You're making and emitting some cold neutrinos right now. And some scientists think that this creates the possibility of chain reactions. Cold neutrinos emitted by earthly reactions can go on to trigger new fusion reactions, which in turn emit more neutrinos.

In essence, any animal, creature, or biological organism that learned to harness these types of neutrinos could sustain energetic reactions with a resonance that good old fossil fuel technology can't accomplish. The reaction would keep going and going as long the conditions were right.

These active neutrinos, both the relic and cold, slow type, are what sustain these fusion reactions naturally. Is it possible that a different lifeform learned to harness their power a long time ago while we humans still rely on fossil fuels and mechanically generated electricity? And can we even imagine that such a thing in nature, creatures powered by dark matter, is possible?

Chapter 6 — Beyond Technology

"A probably reason for the activity may be the correspondence between the chiral characteristics of the electromagnetic fields and the macromolecules of living matter."
—N.E. Nevessky[68]

One of the most significant flaws of our modern era is the belief that ever more sophisticated and faster technology automatically improves our lives and makes us better at understanding and managing our relationships with each other and our environment. We unconsciously use strategies based on the idea of micromanagement and very narrow technical criteria.

However, the opposite might be the case: the more technology we have, the more myopic and narrowly focused we become and less adjusted to our environments. As a result, we end up being largely out of touch with the world and, as I'm suggesting here, almost totally disconnected from the reality of more hidden lifeforms around us: lifeforms that occupy a different phase of matter than we do.

And that's exactly what's happened with our understanding of Sasquatch and related cryptids. Countless Native American tribes and other indigenous peoples worldwide, even the Vikings who discovered America 1000 years ago, have reported seeing and interacting with these creatures over the centuries. Yet as David Paulides says in *The Hoopa Project: Bigfoot Encounters in Northern California*, we "modern" people dismiss this knowledge as superstitious folklore.[69]

Many thousands of credible people in North America alone have reported seeing these beings: on hiking trails, in National Parks, in rural suburbs, near their homes, and on roadways.

Because many of these encounters tend to be fleeting and often don't leave much evidence, they're easy to discount. And then there's the stigma attached to the person who says they saw or encountered such a creature, which acts like a double-whammy: Witnesses are afraid of being laughed at by neighbors, colleagues, and friends. And they don't usually have physical evidence to back up their claims. So the whole thing disappears. Or does it?

I want to suggest another possibility: that we're dealing with an unusual type of creature that transcends the ordinary, familiar rules of existence. They can move in ways that exceed human abilities by a long shot. They can remain invisible, semi-transparent, or even disguise themselves as tree stumps or boulders. And because of their stealthiness, they are hard to take pictures of, even with modern cell phones (which first have to be unlocked, ready to shoot, and focused properly.) It doesn't seem like any technology we possess yet is capable of consistently recording their presence.

If we're interacting with beings made of a different type of matter than us, that would explain why it's so hard to prove they exist. Because the rules of the scientific method, created during the Scientific Revolution a few hundred years ago, were designed for things we can see, touch, and feel. And these creatures have a whole different set of qualities that defy the solidity necessary to fit into modern, ordinary rules of evidence. Despite their size and bulk, their stealthiness and intelligence help them hide from easy observation.

However, just because they're hard to prove empirically doesn't necessarily make them "paranormal" or "demonic" either. It's important to remember that any technology at some point originated in something that nature was already doing, like electricity or magnetism. So what do we do to understand cryptids? We have to look for a different type of evidence that fits another state of matter.

Recognizing a New Type of Matter

I think it's highly likely that recognizing new lifeforms will lead to understanding that technology, as we understand it, has definite limits. As I've witnessed around crop circles, presented with alternative energy configurations, our technologies can short out, overheat, and go caput around other states of matter. I've seen hotel room keys and solder joints in camcorders melt or bend after being in crop circles. And the same type of thing has been reported by bigfoot witnesses. Their cameras and batteries stop working only to be fine a few hours later or the next day when they're back home.

We're told that such a thing can happen from powerful EMP blasts from nuclear weapons: That our cars and everything with transistors could stop working in such a situation.

A related event did happen in 1859 with the global Carrington Event: a geomagnetic storm caused by a massive solar flare that knocked out the telegraph systems of the time, the only electric technology that existed back then. What I'm suggesting here is that cryptids are in fact, creatures that have learned, in some way, to harness the power of cold fusion and gravitational collapse. And more contact with them will lead to the realization that our current technology has an Achilles heel. Our electronic equipment can only operate within a narrow band of electromagnetic parameters, and "supernatural" phenomena often exceed those. And you know this has happened to you when your brand new batteries drain in a few moments.

Just because the bigfoot creatures have "flesh and blood" characteristics doesn't mean they don't also have effects that seem similar to the most advanced technologies we can imagine, such as metamaterials designed to cloak matter. That's the paradox of coherent matter systems: they have features that are both technological and biological at the same time. So, in the next chapter, let's look at some common characteristics of encounters with cryptids, bigfoot, and other phenomena.

Chapter 7—The Fifth State of Matter

"The heck of it is, I can still keep reducing the charge to where it becomes an item that WALKS RIGHT THROUGH THINGS." — Kenneth R. Shoulders[70]

"When the data is real and it keeps repeating itself, there must be a story that's based on reality." — Robert Greenyer[71]

In 2013, I attended a conference in Boulder, Colorado, called the Global Breakthrough Energy Movement, GlobalBEM for short. This conference focuses on alternative types of energy production. One of the presenters was Mark LaClaire, whom I hadn't heard of before, unlike other presenters like UFO researcher and author Richard Dolan: he presented the top ten UFO documents. LaClaire gave a presentation on water cavitation: exciting water at high frequencies to create bubbles that would collapse, releasing a lot of energy. In essence, the bubbles acted to store potential energy from the vibrating water molecules. The bubbles then collapse rapidly, creating Sonoluminescence.[72]

LaClaire told us that sustained cavitation could chain reactions would be release a lot of energy, enough to create a nuclear fusion reaction. Sometimes small glowing dots of light under US patent number

US7297288.
(http://www.rexresearch.com/leclair/leclair.htm)
I learned recently that LaClaire had driven these

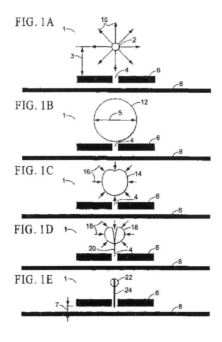

Fig. 17. LeClaire Patent Showing Bubble
Cavitation

processes so hard that they produced ionizing gamma radiation, and he and his business partner had consequently suffered severe injuries.

We now know that such a process of cavitation can create over-driven electron charge clusters to the extent that they produce radioactive elements far past lead (Pb) on the periodic table. But at a lower level of cavitation, you get a safer process characterized by miniature ball lightning and new states of matter.

Telsa and Resonant Chain Reactions

When we consider exotic forms of energy, we often think of Nicola Tesla, the Serbian inventor inspired by seeing a snowball gather massive energy and momentum as it rolled down a hill, eventually destroying everything in its path. However, the truth of the matter, according to Hungarian inventor Dr. George Egely, is that plenty of experimenters, mainly English, were working in these same research areas before the 20th century using high voltages and dusty plasmas (charged dust particles). Unfortunately, many of them were killed in World War I, and this branch of science was all but forgotten. And gradually, these experiments shifted to low-voltage cold fusion type experiments done in small reactors, not the gigantic discharge tubes used by Tesla. (George Egely interview: https://youtu.be/C_0mMpfrsf8)[73]

We're all familiar with the normal three states of matter: solid, liquid, and gas. We learn about these in elementary and high school science classes. Ordinary substances like water can have several phases. Then there are plasmas, the fourth state: hot, ionized gasses that glow when they are charged or subject to an electromagnetic field like an aurora borealis or a neon sign, for example. Straight lightning from clouds is a type of plasma. Plasmas exist in stars and interstellar gas clouds and are the universe's most abundant form of matter. Plasma is also hot.

But there is also the Fifth State of Matter, and it's not as well known. This is a self-organized, coherent type of matter created when a material is subject to

Fig. 18. Aurora Borealis, One Type of Plasma Seen On Earth
(Image by Jean Beaufort, CC0 1.0)

intense pressures or condensed electromagnetically to become ball lightning. Tesla and every other inventor who has dabbled or worked in this field have seen ball lightning in their labs from time to time. And the thing about ball lightning is that it can be cold to the touch: it is not physically burning anything in its environment.

People who have touched metal that ball lightning has recently passed through have noted the metal was like a soft putty for some time but cool. Generally, you'd assume it is hot if you see something glowing. But that's not always the case with ball lightning.

Accounts of ball lightning go back for centuries. It's been seen to go down chimneys, travel along aisles in airplanes, and be visible during and after thunderstorms in areas of mineral-rich soil.[74] Ball lightning is often harmless, but at other times it can cause severe radiation burns or even lethal explosions. The Japanese researcher Takaaki Matsumoto was one of the first to notice that ball lightning seen in nature, and the tiny balls of light seen in lab experiments like Tesla's and Fleishmann and Pons are exactly same thing, just on a smaller scale. Thus, Matsumoto refers to the tiny microscopic orbs as Micro Ball Lightning or MBL.

The entire study of ball lightning has been hampered from the beginning due to its intrinsic danger. The first scientific attempt to study it in 1753 was cut short by the death of one of the scientists involved, Professor

GLOBE OF FIRE DESCENDING INTO A ROOM.

Fig. 19. Ball Lightning Coming Down a Chimney

Fig. 20. Historical Depiction of Ball Lightning
Coming into a Room

George William Richmann, who was killed during a
thunderstorm. We know about this from the work of
Russian scientist Mikhailo Vasil'evich Lomonsov for
whom one of the departments at Moscow State
University is named. Lomonsov, who believed in a
chemical basis for ball lightning, determined that
Richmann's death was not caused by linear lightning
but by a "fireball" that passed through the building
where the lab was set up.[75]

Subsequent research, including 30 cases, was also
done by French physicist, astronomer, and later
politician Francois Arago (1756-1853), who coined the
term "lightning energy condensation."

Instantaneous Magnetization

In 1919 a survey was done on ball lightning accounts and
published in a German book by Walter Brand in 1923.
Among other findings was that ball lightning can magnetize
materials if it passes within very close proximity. It can also

"transport animals and people" and burn or kill animals and people. These effects are summarized in *The Atmosphere and the Ionosphere* by Bychkov et al. (2010).[76]

Bychkov also mentions that ball lightning can pick up objects such as buildings' roofs and instantly vaporize small metal objects such as peoples' rings and bracelets without actually injuring the person wearing them. Again, this tells us that ball lightning is not necessarily hot and more likely cool but organized energy clusters.

Ball lightning's temporary magnetization aspect is fascinating as it suggests that matter is being reorganized at a quantum level by exposure to these energetic orbs:

> One can conclude that BL is not only the physical phenomenon, but geophysical, and geochemical as well. BL appears over and from the Earth mainly after the lightning impact. It can be formed at its impact to metallic and organic subjects. It can be formed during the earthquakes and the volcano activity as well.[77]

And one should add that ball lightning occurs in the absence of any of the above phenomena too, as in Hessdalen, Norway, under completely clear skies.

The US Air Force has been funding research into ball lightning from the 1950s to the present, as seen in their 1993 report where they concluded that it is a natural phenomenon that should be reproducible in a lab.[78] They issued another study in 2003, heavily redacted when it was released to the public, authored by Eric Davis.[79] And if you look at these studies, they're saying that ball lightning is a mysterious natural phenomenon that we don't understand and can't quickly be produced in a lab. So it looks like they didn't make much progress in these ten years.

It's important to remember that many inventors and researchers since Tesla have reached consistent conclusions about the magnetic and gravitational qualities of ball lightning including, Winston H. Bostick (test tube plasmas), John Hutchison (gravitationally fractured metal samples), Kenneth R. Shoulders (Exotic Vacuum Objects). And many Soviet and Russian researchers, including Alexander Parkhomov, B.Y. Bogdanovich, George Mesayats, L.I. Urutskoev, S.V. Adamenko, V.P. Vishneksky, Alexander Shishkin, Michael Solin, and many others. Solin's research is a fascinating case because he attempted to get a patent from the US Patent Office in 1992 for lab-produced charge clusters and ball lightning. The patent office said "no," these things aren't real. They did the same for his 2001 patent in Direct Electricity Production. Yet, in 2021 they granted a related type of patent to Lockheed Martin, one of the world's largest defense contractors.

From the Lab to the Forest

We usually think about something inside a science lab when we talk about ball lightning, charge clusters, EVOs, and the like. As if these were purely technological processes. However, until recently, ball lightning has traditionally been seen in the wild, around thunderstorms, and so forth. But let's say that animals, humans, and creatures in the past had evolved to incorporate this Fifth State of Matter into their biology? What would such creatures be capable of, and would they have abilities superior to ours?

In that case, we'd be seeing this state of matter around us from time to time and calling it something weird or "paranormal." Calling it paranormal marginalizes it, pushing it to the periphery of the idea of reality. But if we refer to it more scientifically as another state of matter, these phenomena don't seem so marginal.

What Does It Take to Create A Ball of Light?

Ball lightning, according to my understanding, is created any time a group of particles, such as electrons, become "monochromatic": i.e., all of the same frequency and temperature. Despite what we were all taught in school, at very close distances, electrons DO NOT REPEL each other from the Coulombic Force; they are attracted to each other.80 This attractive force is so strong that it can form a ball, often called Micro Ball Lightning (MBL). Fryberger at Stanford University, supported by the US Department of Energy, also called it a Mobile Luminous Object (MLO) and Earth Lights (EL), and he said they are all the same thing. It is one of the most densely compacted quantum structures ever seen. This particle packing can happen due to intense pressure, around tectonic and seismic activity, as mentioned above, or where some technological or biological process has squeezed the particles very tightly so that they become very similar to each other and give up their unique characteristics. And the key point is that ball lightning came about in numerous ways. Ball lightning researcher Stanley Singer, followed by Bychkov, said that: "ball lightning is formed by high-energy events such as lightning, volcanoes, tornados, earthquakes and meteors."81

Fryberger at Stanford University, mentioned earlier, even goes so far as to say that ball lightning is so energetically dense that *it can literally penetrate and transcend ordinary matter*. The implications are astounding. (And keep in mind that in the following quote the idea of the Dirac sea is the same as the modern idea of a quantum vacuum):

It should be mentioned that ascribing these currents to a vacuum process implies that they do not depend upon ordinary matter to flow . . . The presence or nonpresence of matter is essentially irrelevant; the particle density in the Dirac sea exceeds that of ordinary matter by many orders of magnitude.[82] (My emphasis)

Ball lightning literally creates its own rules whether at a large or micro scale. Micro ball lightning can create a strong gravitational field (which would explain the interest of the US Air Force in this subject since the 1950s). The electro-nuclear charges are so substantial that the ball is not affected by its environment's other chemical and physical aspects. Takaaki Matsumoto even went so far as to suggest that EVERY Ball Lightning cluster contains a micro black hole, a singularity.[83]

Any organism capable of harnessing such phenomena would also be able to create a host of "weird" effects such as anti-gravity, self-sustaining luminosity (i.e., glowing eyes), electromagnetic field pulses (also creating battery and camera failure). It may sound strange, but these properties, seemingly technological yet outside the realm of established physics, would be a "normal" extension of such biological and physical processes, not genuinely "paranormal."

Ron Morehead describes this happening frequently to their batteries at Sierra camp:

For years I have wondered what these beings are doing with and around electricity. At our Sierra Camp, new batteries would often go dead. The last time this occurred was in 2011. I was at camp alone and had just put fresh lithium batteries in the recorder, yet when I hit the button, I got nothing, dead! This also has happened to Scott Nelson (crypto-linguist) on occasions when we were in camp together.[84].

Why are Bigfoot and Cryptids Seen Around Areas of Frequent Ball Lightning?

It's weird to think that a creature on the Earth could create all these effects, but ball lightning already exists in lab settings and nature. It's simply logical to extend these properties to a living thing also. There was probably a time when electric eels or pyrosomes (glowing sea cucumbers) were also considered "paranormal." Or think of how octopus, cuttlefish, sometimes known as "chameleons of the sea," and other chromatophores can seamlessly blend in with their surroundings. People probably thought these animals were weird, too, when they were first discovered. Discoveries like this are ALWAYS going to seem strange even to inhabitants of Earth a thousand years from now. But even if they seem odd to us now, that doesn't make them any less real.

Need more proof that radically new ideas always seem strange to us? Consider the reaction of a French newspaper to the Wright Brothers. It was very similar to the ridicule of the *New York Times* at the time. The newspaper *Paris Herald* headline in 1906 was "Fliers or Liars?". Well, it turned out they were flyers, but few believed them until a couple of years after they had successfully flown near Dayton, Ohio.[85] Discoveries that later on seem "ordinary" are almost always treated with ridicule and derisive, adverse reactions by the media and public opinion.

I remember seeing a book in the college library where I went to school, and it was from the 1931 and was entitled something like *One Hundred Authors Against Einstein*. Despite all those scientists disagreeing with him, his views prevailed, and Relativity Theory has stood the test of time.

It's no different today. We all think we know the difference between truth and fiction, but it's simply not true. New scientific discoveries always seem strange, bizarre, and unbelievable. Electric, magnetism, and vacuum spaces inside glass bottles were no different. The latter was, at one time, considered supernatural, too.[86] Aristotle had said that there were no vacuums, they were unnatural, and over a millennia later, people still believed him. But we don't think such things because the idea and definition of what's real and what's superstition changes over the centuries.

And, in my view, it will be the same with cryptids and their seemingly extraordinary abilities. There's too much evidence to discount them and too much consistent scientific research to call such creatures supernatural, paranormal, or "demonic." It's much easier to accept that while relatively rare, they exist, perhaps with a different material structure and biology than we're ordinarily used to. There was also a time when airplanes were rare.

The Marley Woods Case

Former Project Bluebook scientist J. Allen Hynek had an associate, Ted Phillips, who studied thousands of "trace case" UFO landing sites. He studied the "Marley Woods" ranch in Southern Missouri for about ten years. He and his colleagues encountered balls of light, unexplained explosions, and strange animals on the property.

He even encountered groups of balls of light, "ambers" as he calls them, as in this case where he saw a pair of the objects together: "They are gliding along so smooth like they're on ice. They weave and bob around tree trunks. And the wind is blowing at 30 to 40 miles per hour and they're flying right into it."[87]

Curiously, some of these balls of light could be seen from one angle and at a distance but were invisible from closer vantage points.

And in one case discussed by Phillips, the rancher went by one of his favorite horses and returned fifteen minutes later. There had been an explosion causing damage to the gate and barn. The horse had been completely destroyed in the blast, and there were only pieces of it left. And yes, this is entirely consistent with ball lightning behavior. Though rare, ball lightning can explode before vanishing: even killing people sometimes from the sudden heat and pressure. Keep in mind this heat is not chemically produced: it's a result of nuclear reactions that transform into heat as energy is released from the ball of light as it comes apart. This energy can also melt wires. Some sources say ball lightning can generate as much as 100 KW of power!

And then there are many reports of balls of light around locations where bigfoot have been seen. A witness named Jeremy from East Texas made the following statement:

> Almost every time, if not every time, I witness the light
> phenomenon, the balls of light, when I'm having bigfoot
> activity. . . There's some kind of correlation between the lights
> and these creatures.[88]

The Fifth State of Matter is All Around Us

While natural ball lightning is admittedly rare and even challenging to create in a lab, that doesn't mean that the conditions that make it are similarly scarce. Ken Shoulders used to say we emit EVOs from our fingertips all the time. You might have noticed it the last time you walked across a rug and touched a doorknob or your pet dog. That spark you felt and perhaps saw visually didn't have enough compression around it to become a long-lasting cluster charge. However, these charge clusters are also created and dissipate quickly around moving water, stream beds, and rotating engines. The difference is that these EVOs disappear almost as soon as they form. Ball lightning, in any form, has been compressed enough for the charge clusters to be monochromatic. Throw in interactions of these clusters with neutrinos streaming in from the cosmos, and you have a recipe for longer-lasting clusters.

Dark Plasmas

In the Ramirez interview referred to earlier, he mentions the idea of "plasma stealth." These are invisible orbs that the CIA observed coming into our atmosphere using infra-red sensing satellite. You can't see them with the naked eye, only the IR detectors on the satellites could.

I think the significance of this is that we've now established that there are invisible states of matter, our intelligence agencies have been interested in them, and it isn't a stretch to imagine biological organisms using this to their advantage in some way. We only need to go back to the Paul Dirac quote earlier. Or as Ian Malcolm said in the movie Jurassic Park "life finds a way."

Ken Shoulders made similar comments about the ability of ball lightning to create connections to "other worlds" and act like a driving force to the world of dark matter:

When seeking a physical analogy for the driving force behind this process, which always occurs to produce a blacker EVO state in the absence of disturbance, a pressure analogy can be evoked. A driving force is seen to occur between the higher-pressure side of our white Universe and the other or black Universe residing in an effectively lower pressure region of space. *It might even be appropriate to signify that the black universe identified here is the much-touted dark matter regime, which is said to dominate in quantity over our normal matter.*[89] (My italics)

Creating Cold Electricity

According to Kouropoulos, electrons can overcome their natural electrostatic repulsion at very close distances of 10^{-13} meters. He refers to this as a magnetic "negative pressure," an attractive force that pulls the particles together.

> For each halving of the mean distance between polarized electrons, the magnetic binding energy grows more than eightfold, attracting surrounding atoms from the periphery. As a result, these cluster about the forming EV, their electrons binding themselves magnetically into the ring. This proceeds until most atomic and molecular shells are half empty, longitudinally squeezed and magnetically polarized piled discs.[90]

The net effect is that the clumps or strings of electrons create a bit of ionizing radiation that converts via the photoelectric effect into electricity. This "runaway magnetization" process leads to a "second type of electricity," also discussed by Ken Shoulders and Takaaki Matsumoto. So we know that ball lightning and coherent matter can create sudden magnetization of metals, which fades away after a day.

One interesting effect of this energetic inversion is "gravitational decoherence" which creates strange effects on mass, thermodynamics: exactly what we see around "paranormal" phenomena including absorption of radiation. This type of energetic phase change would account for the dark blob observed by the three researchers mentioned at Skinwalker Ranch at the beginning of this book.

So basically, the Fifth State of Matter is the natural consequence of electron compression, allowing them to form clusters. This type of matter is responsible for ball lightning and other "strange" phenomena, including reversals of normal thermodynamic processes. We would expect sudden pockets of cold temperatures, dark patches where there should be light, and even gravitational anomalies, including objects seemingly floating in the air.

Time Loss

Some observers have reported time loss during ball lightning encounters, similar to what happens around some UFOs. This might be the result of the effects of intense magnetization on the human body and brain. On the other hand, changing the permittivity of space itself and its natural electrical conductivity might also change how time is perceived.

Alternate Magnetic States

As electrons cluster together in a tight bunch, they create another weird state of matter: magnetic monopoles. Paul Dirac argued that these should exist somewhere in the universe if electricity exists. Magnetic monopoles are the magnetic equivalent of electrical flow as they only have a north or south pole but not both. The types of magnetic monopoles seen in ball lightning are not the fundamental, permanent type that Dirac suggested, but more like quasi or pseudo-monopoles in that they are short-lived. They create magnetic areas in places where you wouldn't expect it. Magnetic monopoles leave things that look like "caterpillar tracks" behind as they move across a surface.

Feelings of Fear and Danger

Another exciting aspect of ball lightning documented over the centuries are feelings of fear that accompany these sightings. This seems to be true regardless of whether the object causes physical injury.

And another curious aspect of ball lightning is its ability to play "cat and mouse" with people and animals. It's almost as if the ball can follow small perturbations in the Earth's background electromagnetic fields or the electrostatic gradients inside houses.[91]

Ball lightning can also emit narrow beams of light, and flame tips, either inside other objects like planes or on the ground.[92]

Are UFOs and Ball Lightning the Same Phenomenon?

There is a definite continuum between UFOs, orbs, and ball lightning so much that it is sometimes impossible to tell the difference. Retired CIA officer John Ramirez claims that UFOs have an orb-like state, sometimes only visible in the infra-red spectrum, that is detectable by spy satellites. And as we have noted above, ball lightning can have an interactive quality that makes it appear sentient.

But by and large, ball lightning is much smaller than UFOs which can be as large as football field-length battleships in the sky. In contrast, most ball lightning tends to be one foot and half in diameter or less. Yet, some other ball lightning can rarely be up to six meters.[93] And in the upper atmosphere, ball lightning can be as big as 100 meters and last for several hours.[94]

And, of course, UFOs sometimes have occupants or living beings associated with them. And yet these UFOs' ability to seemingly defy gravity, give off light of different colors, accelerate at rapid speeds, debilitate electronics, create sudden electromagnetic effects, and bob up and down give them a lot in common with ball lightning. So even though we'd like a clear boundary between the two phenomena, we can't say what it is at this point.

"Ball Lightning Radio"

Clearly, there's a lot of energy around areas of ball lightning and it seems that cryptids have picked up on this energy to "ride the rails" for free so to speak. It's possible that the extra energy provided by ball lightning allows them to phase in and out of specific geographical areas. Plus you could add in the energy they might be getting from cosmic active neutrinos mentioned in earlier chapters and they would clearly be in a different space than we are. Places similar to Skinwalker and Marley Woods mentioned by Kelleher and Knapp include a ranch in Elbert County in Colorado, Dulce, New Mexico, and an area on the East side of the Cascade Mountains in Washington State. So these areas could be seen as "portals" in the sense that there are highly concentrated geological energetic processes going on just like in Yellowstone, though in that case it's due to a caldera below the surface providing continuous volcanic activity as seen in this still image in Fig. 21 taken June 2, 2017.

Fig. 21. Ball Lightning seen in the Yellowstone area (Still from YouTube Video)

The presence of concentrated energy in one area is like a frequency which has its own lifeforms, phenomena, and strange events. Kind of like a parallel reality powered by electron clusters. You could think of it like a radio station on your AM or FM dial. The station plays a lot of shows but they're all at the same frequency. Similarly, these portal areas have a characteristic "quantum" frequency that allows a particular cast of characters to make their appearance there.

Chapter 8—The Crop Circle Connection: Sudden Battery, Camera and Electronic Failure

In my previous book, *Opening Minds*, and on my YouTube channel, I've discussed some of the strange battery draining and electronics destroying effects of crop circles and patterns I've experienced. This includes the Devil's Den formation at Fyfield Down, UK, in 1999, where I saw three electronic devices affected by the crop formation within about 1/2 hour. I later talked to witnesses who had visited the formation and said their cameras didn't work for several months after visiting the formation and another who reported instant battery failure in the crop circle. What accounts for such phenomena?

In other crop formations throughout the years, both in the US and the USA, I've seen photos of mysterious glowing areas in crop circles that I had made with a group of researchers. Countless other formations created weird effects on electronic devices, such as this electronic watch with a built-in compass that refused to point North while the visitor was in a crop circle near Avebury, Wiltshire. (See Figures 22 and 23.)

Fig. 22. Electronic Compass Stops Working in the Avebury Crop Circle, 2006
(Photo by Author)

Fig. 23. Electronic compass no longer points North
(Photo by Author)

Strange Magnetic Phenomenon in Crop Circles and Cryptids

In 2000, researcher Colin Andrews and an engineer, Jean-Noel Auburn, took readings with a magnetometer at a crop circle in Milton Hill Farms, Wiltshire UK. The patterns of high magnetic activity were quite strong according to Andrews. Surprisingly the areas of highest magnetic activity were mirrored in the shape of the pattern which was a Celtic cross. Yet, this was a manmade formation as Ron Russell and I discovered when we visited the small town. I ended up learning the names of all five people who made the crop circle. It still created this magnetic pattern.

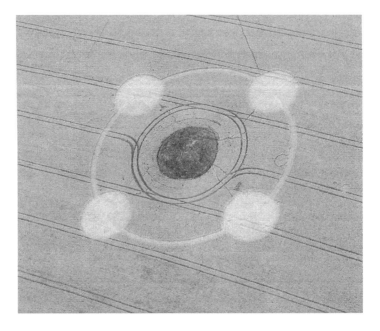

Fig. 24. Milton Hill Farms Crop Formation, 2000
(Photo by Author)

In another case, Ron Russell, a crop circle researcher, told me he had his magnetic compass spin around unexplainably in a crop formation in a field across from the manmade earth mound Silbury Hill in 1993. He had gone into the formation and met with other researchers, Freddy Silva and Paul Vigay. He went back to his car to get a compass and as he approached the crop circle again, he told me his compass "spun around like a motor."

In the Avebury Trusloe "Nested Scorpion" formation in 1994, Ron had a time-slip experience. He went into the formation to take pictures and ran out of film. He decided to go back to his car and, on the way, felt as if he had entered another century 500 years ago. The wheat had a different appearance, the tramways disappeared, and he ran into short people speaking an older English language that was barely comprehensible. Retrieving the camera film from his vehicle, he returned to the crop circle and felt like he had been gone for a long time, perhaps 30 minutes to an hour.

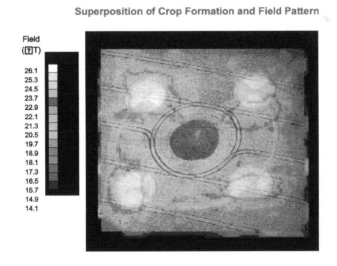

Fig. 25. Milton Hill Farms Crop Circle Magnetism, 2000
(Photo and Scientific Overlay ©2000 by Colin Andrews and Jean-Noel Aubrun)

However, when he approached the group he had been with, they said he had only been gone for five minutes at most.

Fig. 26. Silbury Hill Crop Circle Caused a Magnetic Compass to Spin Around "like a Motor."
(Photo ©1993 by Ron Russell)

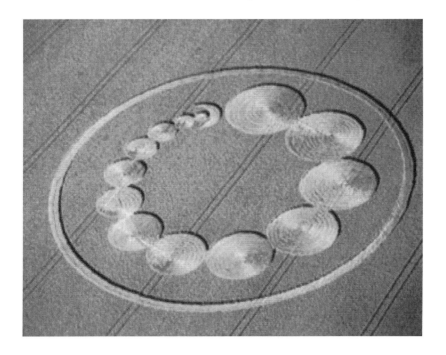

Fig. 27. Crop Formation at Avebury Trusloe, 1994.
(Image © by Ron Russell)

Fig. 28. Strange Effects on Film Camera in Kansas Crop Circle, 2002
(Photos © by Ron Russell)

And yet, at another formation we made in 2002 in Kansas, there were inexplicably excess exposures in the film emulsion of a Nikon manual SLR camera. The camera never malfunctioned before or after these photos were taken.

This strange magnetic activity suggests that crop circle patterns are somehow generating Exotic Vacuum Objects or something similar like tiny ball lightnings, altering the magnetic field in their vicinity.

I'm convinced this is also happening with some cryptids, as we'll see in the next chapter. I've spoken with many bigfoot researchers who say they've experienced battery-draining effects in the areas of bigfoot activity. And it's not usual for people fleeing hostile bigfoot activity to find that their car engine won't start, just as the bigfoot approaches their vehicle.

Whirlwinds and Plasma Vortices

In 1982, a bicycle shop owner named Ray Barnes in Westbury, UK noticed a strange air flow moving through wheat fields followed by a simple crop pattern. And even more curiously, he reported paranormal phenomena following the event, including time distortions and shadow people. Japanese researcher Oktsuki suggested these whirlwinds were created by plasma vortices descending from the sky: a perspective also adopted by UK researcher Terrence Meaden. One of the original explanations for crop circles in the 1980s was that atmospheric plasma vortexes created them.

Takaaki Matsumoto of Sapporo University, Hokkaido, Japan, also witnessed and reported this phenomenon in his papers about cold fusion. He says small crop circles were created in wheat fields near his university over three days of thunderstorms, and Matsumoto attributed this to ball lightning seen around thunderstorms.

Andrew Collins in his book, *The New Circlemakers*, states that he believes the paranormal aspects of the

Barnes' circles were due to his proximity to Warminster, UK, an area of known UFO sightings.[95] While I can't discount this possibility, there's another explanation: once you've created vortices and plasmas, you have all the ingredients you need for Coherent Matter Phenomena. Spinning vortices is one way of producing charge clusters that entail cold neutrinos, AKA dark matter.

So one of the possibilities here is that the same phenomena that created the crop circles in the first place, spinning vortexes, all left some dark matter behind in the soil, making time and space distortions.

Now, as crop circles developed in the 1990s, the patterns became increasingly complex (due to human involvement, in my view), which led to the demise of the plasma vortex theory. However, I think it's likely that plasma vortexes create SOME crop circles, as in this pattern below that showed up below the Westbury Whitehorse, UK, in 2010. The splayed-out wheat stalks suggest a force coming down on the crop from above. This circle-making force would be not just due to winds from the vortexes but from charge clusters producing their gravitational forces, as Takaaki Matsumoto has outlined (See Figures 29 and 30.)

Fig. 29. Crop Circle
Formation, Westbury
Whitehorse, 2010
(Photo by Author)

I can't say the exact percentage of crop circles made by plasmas and what percent are made by human circle makers (though in recent decades, I'd say it was much more of the latter). However, I know that UFOs and unexplained flying discs flatten plants if they get close to a field.

In my interview with Louise Voves in *Black Swan Ghosts,* a woman from North Idaho, she was emphatic that she saw a flying disc over a flower meadow in the 1970s near Usk, Washington, that flattened the meadow plants "flat as a pancake" and bent them at 90 degrees.

But the main point here is that any rapid compression of plant material is likely to create some charge clusters leading to the possibility of electron vortices at the site. Moreover, the pattern left behind in the plant material might interact with dark matter in the form of relic neutrinos. And this suggests the exciting possibility that crop circles interact directly with dark matter energies. I mentioned this idea in my paper "Investigation into Dark Energy as the Cause of Anomalous Electromagnetic Activity Observed in the Vicinity of Crop Formations."[96]

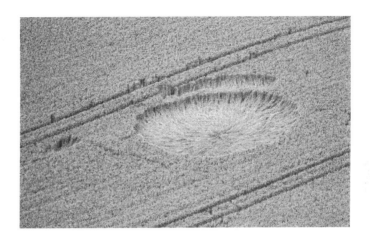

Fig. 30. Closeup of Crop Circle Formation,
Westbury Whitehorse, 2010 (Photo by Author)

So even though this is a book about dark matter and cryptids, we can probably say that the subject of weirdness around dark matter extends to crop circles, UFOs, and probably other phenomena that we're not even aware of yet.

Sure, it's a big jump to connect all these topics, but it would also explain many things we haven't been able to talk about so far. Why do people see cryptids around areas of UFOs (at places like Skinwalker Ranch); why do many of these strange phenomena affect batteries and cameras; why are there biological effects around them, sometimes with harmful effects on people exposed to these energies.

I've received a lot of hostility over the years from researchers on both sides of this issue. Those who favor the UFO-caused or ball lightning/orbs idea of what causes crop circles think I lean too far on the side that they're all manufactured. Those who believe they are all manmade think I go too far to look for other explanations. A well-known UK researcher, now passed on, once told me that if I didn't stop my research into manmade circles, he would no longer interact with me. Plus, I would be permanently barred from presenting again at crop circle conferences. Talk about having a closed mind! That's not science, it's a type of religious fundamentalism.

The truth is that crop circles have a plethora of causes including all the usual suspects like human circle makers, some who are very well-intentioned and others who aren't; plus balls of light; and possibly ET craft (or whoever is actually in them if they're indeed occupied with sentient beings).

My Ball Lightning Sighting Near a Crop Circle

In 1998, I was in the UK on a crop circle tour. One evening, I found myself on Knapp Hill with another tour guest, Doug, from Pueblo, Colorado. It was just getting dark, and we were looking down toward East Field, where there was a giant crop circle, and it was getting too dark to see the formation. Suddenly, to our right, we both saw a small, grapefruit-sized blue ball of light resting on the grass, about ten feet away. It looked like it was being fed energy from the ground beneath it: there was a slight shape distortion where it touched the ground. It was there for about 2 to 3 seconds and then vanished.

What do crop circles have to do with bigfoot and cryptids? The way I see it, reality can be more complex than you think it is. Things don't always fit in your self-created or socially mandated "reality boxes," to use remote viewer Ingo Swann's phrase. And a more substantial possibility exists that the same energetic roots connect these seemingly disparate phenomena. This could be why you get some of the same anomalies in crop circle areas, UFO encounters, and areas of bigfoot activity. Battery failure, camera malfunction, and general electronic mayhem could be the calling card of dark matter and cosmic forces driving ordinary matter into new states of coherency and energetic potency. And these condensed, coherent states of matter create weird effects that seem paranormal and often supernatural to us.

So let's move on and see what it's like to encounter cryptid creatures and some side effects you're likely to experience.

Chapter 9—Dark Matter Lifeforms

"It moved faster than you would believe." — Richard Boston about witnessing a bigfoot in California[97]

"You could a feel tremor every time its feet hit the ground." —Jim, truckdriver, commenting on his encounter at a rest stop[98]

"The first thing I thought was 'bear" but right away I realized this black shaggy thing wasn't a bear. This thing was smart. I've never seen animal trying to pick up protection as it fled. The proportions of the torso - it looked more stocky than anything else. I noticed the arms swung more than a human's would and it didn t have elbows cocked. " — Bob 'Action' Jackson, former Yellowstone Park Ranger[99]

In 1978, I went on a "teen camping tour" of the West, which was somewhat common for East Coast kids like myself in high school. Our first stop was a grassland area in Nebraska and then the Devil's Tower area of Wyoming.

We then went on a backpacking trip in the Montana section of the Northwest corner of Yellowstone National Park. We hiked several miles from the highway and started to pitch our tents and make camp. One of the kids went off on his own about 1/4 mile from the remote backcountry campsite. He came back shaken and scared. Between rapid breaths, he said something had lunged at him from the trees. We all thought it had to be a bear; what else could it be out there in Yellowstone? So that was the strange thing about it. He didn't think it was a bear. As he was gasping for air, all he would say was: "I don't know what it was." We all tried to convince him he had seen a bear, but he wouldn't agree. He was still upset several hours later, and we were all told not to go out by ourselves away from the campsite.

We were in Green River State Park in southern Utah a few weeks later. We were sitting around a campfire in the evening just talking. Suddenly, I felt like I had sneezed, but I wasn't sure if someone else had sneezed and I had just heard it. But what happened next was even stranger. For a split second later, there was a horizontal crack of light, and then I was in another world, a desert scene with a tall reptilian looking at me from about 15 yards away. The creature was male, tall, and muscular. It spoke in a low, growling voice. Then it all disappeared. I was back at the campfire with the other kids. What had just happened? To this day, I still can't explain it. Was it real or a hallucination?

What do these experiences suggest? I believe we're having encounters from time to time that we can't easily explain. And generally, we tend to shuffle and filter these "unknown" encounters into a more familiar mental category, even though this might seem like a stretch. By glossing over these experiences and substituting the generally socially acceptable definitions, we avoid thinking about them. But once we look more closely, we'll see we had an encounter with the big unknown.

Witnesses to bigfoot and cryptids, I believe, experience the same type of disbelief I experience over my desert encounter. Did it happen? Was it all in my imagination? Perhaps my encounter was an illusion, and it didn't leave footprints, hair, and other evidence behind. Human minds have a "boggle point" and similar reactions to sudden stressful encounters, and we're all pretty much the same in this regard. It's not just that you might not believe someone else's story: they might not believe it either! But that doesn't mean it didn't happen.

So, if less than 5 percent of our universe is visible to us, as cosmologists tell us, the rest being dark matter, dark energy, and non-visible, "non-baryonic" ordinary matter, why should it be any different from the lifeforms around us? Perhaps what we think of as "reality" on our planet is only 5 percent of what's out there. We live in a society with delusional self-confidence about what's real and what's not. There's a definite left-brain bias, and we can't imagine what other people experience outside the accepted paradigm. But they have these "hard-to-accept" experiences—a lot of them. And typically, they don't tell the rest of us about what happened to them. And that's the trap of modern thinking: to believe that nothing's real except what experts on your favorite shows, podcasts, and blogs have told you is accurate. As if these experts don't have their own biases, agendas, and prerogatives that could affect their viewpoints.

You Don't Know What You Don't Know

Kurt Gödel, a mathematician at Princeton's Advanced Study Institute, is known for creating the "incompleteness theorem": the idea that no matter how good your logic, there are always things that are true that you won't be able to prove exist within your logical system. Your formal knowledge will also always be incomplete. It has become known as "Gödel's Incompleteness Theorem." A way to imagine this is that, at the center of every system of knowledge and logic, is a swirling black hole of the unknown. And no matter how hard we try, we can never erase those unknowns.

As mathematician Gregory Chaitin explains, the unknown is never very far away from us:

> It is easy to show that there are infinitely many prime numbers . . . but in any direction you go you quickly get to results which are conjectured, but which no one knows how to prove. So the frontiers of knowledge are nearby, in fact, extremely close.[100]

Chaitin says that so-called "Formal Axiomatic Systems," complete systems of knowledge once considered the prized achievement of science and mathematicians like mathematician David Hilbert would never fully describe reality. There will always be holes in these paradigms.

The attitude expressed by Chaitin reinforces the notion that we are overconfident, to the point of fallibility, that our theories completely explain reality or that we even understand the full scope of life around us on planet Earth. There will always be a reality beyond our current paradigm.

If you're wondering why this is true: it's the product of mathematical set theory that will consistently produce illogical outcomes above and beyond what you expect them to do. Any set of axioms, theorems, and proofs will never be able to self-reference or explain themselves. As an example, consider the following set of sentences:

"The following sentence is true. The previous sentence is false."

Taken apart, they make sense: taken together, they form an endless, nonsensical loop. And the same is true for every idea produced by logic and reason alone. At some point, any set of ideas will break down into individually logical yet collectively meaningless feedback loops.

The Great Disconnect from Reality: How did it get this way?

There's a saying I'm fond of: *"When all you have is a hammer, everything looks like a nail."* In other words, increasingly linear, additive, technical thinking over the centuries has led us to look at things in narrow, myopic ways. Max Weber, the German sociologist a century ago, called it "rationalization." By that, he meant leaving less and less of life to chance. In other words, "micromanagement," as we now call it. This increasingly focused perspective, nano-culture, has a significant downside we seldom consider. We won't look at anything outside the box, any phenomena that don't easily fit into simplistic, techno-rational categories: Phenomena like bigfoot, cryptids, remote viewing, "psychic functioning," and strange effects of UFOs. So we're effectively blind-sided by our narrowly focused thinking and ideas. Rather than expand our horizons, we've effectively narrowed them to fit in an increasingly limited paradigm of "practical" and "modern" living.

And so it is with cryptids. They've been described by thousands of Native American tribes, many of whom couldn't even converse with one another. Yet they all had a name for bigfoot. There have been thousands of witness reports on the BFRO.net site alone, including law enforcement officers, national park rangers, members of the military, and first responders. And the reports are remarkably consistent regarding the physical characteristics and behavior of the cryptids, be it bigfoot, dogman, or the Little People. So you could say that all these thousands of Native American tribes and modern witnesses are delusional, but I doubt it.

In his two books about his experiences with bigfoot at the Sierra Camp, Ron Morehead describes many qualities of these creatures and the weird things that happen around them. These include the following that other researchers have also experienced.

Batteries Going Dead

Rapidly depleted batteries are one of the most surprising features of bigfoot encounters: I would have thought this could only happen around electromagnetic technologies. But it is often reported around bigfoot sightings, and Ron Morehead experienced this at the Sierra Camp on several occasions. It is strangely reminiscent of batteries draining and cars stalling near UFO sightings. And it's likely caused by a similar phenomenon.

I talked to a witness from Colorado who had an encounter near Estes Park. She was visiting a friend's cabin in Drake, Colorado. Her phone went dead immediately after taking photos of an area where she thought she heard strange sounds, like children playing, a baby crying, and tree limbs breaking. She and her husband had gone to check on a friend's summer cabin, and he stayed behind while she went down a path to look at it. She noticed that sounds were always about 50 feet in front of her as she moved down the trail. She told me she later felt something like "brain drain" for a day and a half after the encounter, which is not uncommon for bigfoot witnesses. She was so confused immediately afterwards that she could barely find her way back to her car, where her husband was waiting. He had to hit rocks together so she could hear him.

At the "Bailey Bigfoot Conference" in May 2021, conference organizer Jim Myers of the Sasquatch Outpost mentioned that once, several cars in the same trailhead parking lot had their batteries drained while they were looking for the creature in the Bailey area. Stan Gordon, mentioned in this book, talks explicitly about the strange effects of bigfoot on cars' electrical systems, including headlights dimming when they're nearby.[101]

Here's a typical encounter that Gordon mentions from Hillside, Pennsylvania, August 25th, 1973. A boy on a mini-bike had his vehicle stall suddenly at around 8 pm. "He then heard a snorting sound coming from behind him." He turned and then saw an 8-foot creature with eyes the size of ping-pong balls standing only 5 feet away from him.

And if you read the literature of witness accounts, you'll find similar stories of car batteries going dead, at least temporarily, while bigfoot are near.

Now I can hear you saying: "but Simeon, isn't cold fusion a type of technology and bigfoot are biological entities like us: So how are they connected?"

Fair enough. I'm saying that cold fusion is based on an abundant, natural process found on Earth and throughout the universe. So it's no surprise that some creatures, maybe even human-like, "figured it out," or at least evolved to incorporate the value and benefits of dense energy packing into their lives. It's probably just an outcome of evolution on a grand scale, and for some reason, we don't access these processes in the same way or have collectively chosen to ignore them.

Static Charges and Electronics Failure

A professional nature sound recorder and her partner Dan were at the Boiling River Hot Springs in the Northern part of Yellowstone Park at night: a place they had been to with no strange occurrences. While Dan told her about the mysterious "Yellowstone Hum" people have reported hearing over the years, they started to feel a static charge buildup. Dan suddenly and inexplicably passed out in the hot springs, and the woman noticed a figure standing in the nearby tree line. While dragging Dan back to the car 1/2 mile away, she saw a blue glow from the trees where the figure had been and blue balls of light rolling down nearby slopes. A bull moose charged through the area with sparks coming from its feet. They could make it back to the car, but the ignition would not start. A glowing blue creature then approached the car shedding copious amounts of light into the vehicle. Its long hair was standing on end along with the blue glow. The beast then left, and the car started. They both felt ill the next day. (Wilson, 2019).

Ron Morehead, a witness to "Biggie" type creatures in the 1970s at the Sierra Camp in California, wrote about experiencing battery failure:

> We had our cameras, all something going wrong with them, our batteries would go dead up there [in the Sierras], Scott Nelson, the crypto-linguist that rode up there, he would have his batteries failing, he went up there with enough batteries to last forever, but also they wouldn't work. My batteries, my brand-new lithium batteries. This was in 2011. I was by myself, when I heard this big pop right outside my tent. I really think it might've not been something hitting a tree, like I originally thought, but maybe something energetically coming out of the tree.[102]

As I mentioned in Chapter 8 on crop circles, we've seen this strange battery-draining effect many times as we approached or entered crop circles. Again, I think it's the same electrically anomalous phenomena we're talking about here, whether in crop circles, UFOs, or bigfoot. Russian researcher Alexander Shishkin calls it "explosive unpacking" of electron clusters, which will quickly destroy electronics and batteries.

Speed

One thing you get over and over from reading and listening to bigfoot encounters is an incredible speed that the creatures move. It's faster than anyone can imagine, sometimes keeping pace with cars moving at highway speeds.

Igor Burtsev describes a case in Russia where the witnesses hit a bigfoot on the road, which then got up and chased their car as it drove away. The bigfoot caught up and smashed out their rear window. This incident was captured on video, and you can hear the occupants screaming as the creature rides the tail end of their vehicle. A review of bigfoot contact cases shows many similar accounts.[103]

One witness I know, Teri, was with her boyfriend in Utah in the mountains above Salt Lake, in an area called Cotton Creek. They went to a campsite, closed for the season, but they had found the gate open and went anyway. First, they heard a "long, deep, scary, guttural, and fierce" howl off in the distance. Teri at first thought it was a bear, but they then realized no bear could howl so long and deep like that. She said it sounded more like a cross between a lion and bear but more intense and prolonged. Then, faster than any animal could run, another loud, long growling howl very close by. Then they heard the sound of a "freight train moving through a forest" with crashing sounds and branches breaking, which abruptly stopped behind a tree just beyond the light cast by the campfire. Whatever it was, Teri got the feeling it was standing on two legs. She and her boyfriend then got into their truck as quickly as possible. They turned their truck around and then got their things and quickly left.

Some people describe cryptid motions so fast that the creatures look like cartoon characters. "It moved faster than you could believe" said guest Robert Boston on the nightly *Spaced Out Radio* show with host Dave Scott. Others have described the speed as similar to that of a hummingbird.[104] How does something weighing over 800 pounds and built like an NFL linebacker move as fast as a hummingbird?

A witness on *Sasquatch Chronicles* said his father wanted to shoot at the giant hairy creatures in their front yard and did so once (the family had lost all their goats and chickens to these "animals"); they started to move faster and quicker from tree to tree. There was no way to aim after the first shot, ever again.[105]

Is this speed a function of their size, or is it "supernatural"? Usually, the fastest animals on the planet are smaller, like falcons which can reach speeds of 200 mph in a dive, or cheetahs at 75 mph. But a giant, heavy biped? The fastest human running speed is around 30 mph.

In another case, hikers in Oregon saw a creature pacing them on the opposite side of a river. They said it looked like an Olympic athlete that never took its dark eyes off them as it ran parallel to them up the slope along the river. The next day they attempted to look where the creature had been running. They were amazed to find it filled with large rocks, trees, and tree stumps and couldn't even imagine walking at a steady pace in such terrain. How could anything run over that type of ground?

Another witness, Scott, a truck driver, saw the creature from a bridge in York County, PA, perhaps 30 feet away. Another motorist pulled up. Both watched as the beast stood up and turned towards them. It hit the ground with its fist, growled, and then took off running on all fours, almost looking like a spider. As Scott said: "It took off like a rocket. Like a gazelle on steroids."[106] For such a massive creature to possess such extraordinary speeds suggest incredible strength or special energetic abilities.

This extraordinary speed also applies to sightings of dogman, where witnesses are baffled by the creature's rapid movements. In one case, a couple hiking in Sequoia National Park saw a two-legged creature that looked like a cross between a German Shepherd with black fur and a human being slightly hunched over on the trail in front of them, about 30 feet away. As it appeared to get ready to charge them, they both ran back in the other direction. However, 40 yards back the other way; they now saw an identical-looking creature facing two other hikers. They had no idea if it was a similar creature or the same one, apparently having teleported to the new location after disappearing behind them.[107]

And it may be more than speed and stealth that makes cryptids hard to photograph. As rock musician, film director, and founder of To The Stars Academy, @TomDelonge recently tweeted: "Have you ever considered Bigfoot *is* blurry? And maybe that is the photographic issue?"[108]

Telepathic Communication and Mental Influence

People who've been around bigfoot-type creatures sometimes report a "mind to mind" connection with them. Sometimes this occurs around their dwellings or where they're camping. Curiously enough, the creatures seem interested in getting people to come outside, both children and adults. Now, this isn't an audible voice that you hear physically. It's more like a type of mental talk that registers in your brain. You can hear something but can't identify the source, and you can only tell it's not coming from your mind.

Many witnesses report hearing this voice talking in their heads or at least feeling like they are listening to a voice in their head. One person who had a Sasquatch trailing them in Yellowstone described its speech as sounding like a "muddy voice."[109] Others have described the voice in their head as sounding mechanical, methodical, and computer-like.[110]

As the previously mentioned Yellowstone thru-hiker said: "I was walking along, . . . when I heard a voice talking to me, but it wasn't like I could hear it with my ears as much as in my mind."[111] In this case, the voice repeatedly told the hiker to go off the main trail he was on. The hiker could see another path veering off, but his common sense told him not to go there. Later, when he checked Google Maps, he saw no trail there! Something had attempted to trick him into going the wrong way.

Barb, a woman who took my Resonant Viewing training classes and came on one of the crop circle tours in the UK, told me a story of encountering a Sasquatch telepathically. She was upstairs in a house near Colorado Springs when she heard a loud scream and saw a red-haired creature in her mind's eye. Her roommate simultaneously saw such a creature through the kitchen's French doors. In one step, the bigfoot went over their balcony to the ground. Her roommate confirmed that the beast had, indeed, looked precisely like Barbara had seen it in her mind. (https://youtu.be/gYpB0SATwCQ)

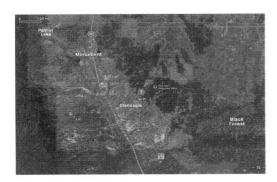

Fig. 31. Location of Barb's Sighting near Gleneagle, Colorado (Image ©2022 by Apple Maps

Fig. 32. Barb with Drawing that she says Looks Similar to the Creature who Visited her Porch Deck (Photo by Author)

Fig. 33. Photo of House Showing Porch
Deck Where Creature was Seen
(Photo ©2021 by Google Maps)

Another woman, Julie, who took my resonant viewing classes in 2019 in Coeur D'Alene, Idaho, described something she experienced in Indiana as a young child. In the summertime, she noticed it became suddenly quiet as she saw a white-haired, man-like, muscular, hairy creature with a sloping dome-shaped head and no neck at the end of her street-picking blackberries. "The face was brown like leather, its eyes piercing black ...a broad flat nose." It saw her but posed no threat. All of a sudden, she said it felt like a "spell was broken," and it ran away. When she told her parents what she had seen, they mocked her and suggested she had seen a neighbor in a fur coat! In the summer, no less. She reported the sighting to the BFRO. (http://www.bfro.net/GDB/show_report.asp?id=26587)

But an even stranger event occurred years later when she had moved to Alabama. She was involved in repairing her bathroom and needed a pipe wrench. She was so beside herself trying to fix the leak she was crying. She hadn't talked to anyone about this. She suddenly felt compelled to go outside to compose herself, and right smack in the middle of her driveway, there was the exact type of wrench she needed! Coincidence? Possibly, but this sort of event is not rare in the world of bigfoot-human interactions. Other witnesses say that their vehicles had major body dents repaired overnight and found flat rocks neatly stacked nearby the next morning. (https://youtu.be/Kji-qY_xPWQ)

Fig. 34. Jules Describes her Bigfoot Encounters, YouTube Video

Something showing up when you need it, a physical object perhaps, is known as an "apport." There is a long history of apports in the study of paranormal phenomena. Russell Targ even mentioned this in conjunction with a visit by psychic Uri Geller to the SRI labs in the early 1970s. But who knew it also happens near bigfoot encounters?

Some witnesses report perceiving strong suggestions to step outside their trailers or homes when the bigfoot creatures are around. Sometimes, as their fear is growing that something isn't right, they'll also get a message in their minds to slow down and turn around. Witnesses recall having to fight such thoughts to get away. Then afterward, they feel that brain fog mentioned above.[112]

A deeper level of such contact is the so-called "gifting relationships" where you leave something for them, like apples, for example, and they, in return, leave you a rock, a crystal, or even something yummy like mummified field mice braided in the grass, we're told.[113]

It's incredible to me how consistent these gifts from the creatures are. In any case, empathetic relations between humans and bigfoots seem to be a real thing.

One of the earliest reports of this occurrence is the Fred Beck "Ape Canyon" story from 1924. Beck describes how his group of five gold miners was attacked in their cabin by "apemen." His story takes an unusual turn when he describes various psychic and supernatural experiences following the attack, including a pencil from his home appearing in his hand when he needed one. Beck concludes that the Sasquatch are not purely physical beings.[114]

Sudden Quiet

So pay attention if this happens while you're out in the woods or hiking in the mountains. Many people report this sensory experience right before a UFO or bigfoot encounter.

Terry Lovelace and friend Toby mentioned previously in Chapter 3 noticed unusual calm and quiet right before sighting the triangular UFO above their campsite. Even the crickets had stopped chirping.

David Paulides describes a camping trip with Dad in 1968 in Northern California. They had hiked down to a creek where the father had camped for decades. Shortly after arriving at their campsite after a long hike, they smelled smoke and discovered a neatly constructed small fire made of small twigs on a sand bank. David noticed a strange quiet in the area: "There were no birds chirping, no squirrels running around, no sound except the creek. It was almost as if a vacuum had sucked all of noise out of the atmosphere except for the water running over the boulders."[115] While Paulides says they never saw a bigfoot or any other creature, there were no markings or tracks in the sand around the small fire. The whole area just felt eerie.

A witness hiking in Big Bear, California, in 1999 noticed a sudden silence in the area shortly after seeing a strange figure observing her in the woods. It approached her later, and she described it as looking like a colossal caveman, covered in long hair, on all fours making whooping sounds. Just before it approached her, she said: "I noticed the crows were no longer anywhere to be found . . . Everything had become so eerily quiet, even for that time of day."[116]

A landowner in Malvern, Arkansas reported a similar feeling after hearing loud sounds coming from the barn: "When he got to the barn he stopped to listen for any sound of whatever made that crash. It was eerily quiet, no bugs, frogs or any sound at all. Complete silence."[117]

In his book *Bigfoot, UFOs and the Paranormal: True Encounters*, recalls having an experience similar to the one described by Lynn above. Buckner said he was sitting in his truck by a campsite waiting to meet other hunters when something approached.

> I could feel my skin tingling like a slight jolt of electricity—a peculiar sense. That's when I noticed that it had gone silent. The crickets, cicadas, and bullfrogs—all stopped. Nothing. Nothing but deathly silence.[118]

He could feel a presence just a few inches from his vehicle, and the next thing he remembers, he was at a store in a nearby town. Everything in his truck was intact, but he had no idea how he got there.

Does sudden quiet fit in our ideas here? Yes, it does. Coherent matter is geometrically organized, and you would expect acoustic effects when particles become correlated in unusual ways. The principle is called "Phase Conjugation" and is well known within the science of acoustics. Acoustic waves can reinforce or cancel each other out, in which case you'll get dead silence. Visit a high-end recording or practice studio, and you're likely to see acoustic construction designed to cancel out sounds.

Is that what is going on here with these "paranormal" encounters? Are witnesses seeing and experiencing the advanced effects of coherent matter objects as they approach from over the horizon? I can't say for sure, but it sure fits the other symptoms we've discussed here.

Another possibility is that both UFOs and cryptids affect the structure of space-time in their local vicinity, so time is not flowing in a typical way. Or that somehow the acoustic signals are not getting to you normally, creating a blanket of uncomfortable quiet.

Dark Matter and Resonance

But is all this a "dark matter type" of phenomena? Quite possibly, if we're familiar with the arguments of Dr. Alexander Parkhomov in his book *Space. Earth. Human.*[119] He devotes the final section of his book to "psychic related" (my words) phenomena. And if we understand the significance of active neutrinos, then it's easy to understand that any life form that is connected to dark matter will inherently have natural "telempathic" abilities. Yes, telempathic like in ability to empathize.

Why would this be so? Well, the cosmic neutrino background neutrinos were all created at the exact same moment in time, so they're all quantum entangled with each other. And since they're raining down on us all the time from every direction in the universe, at a density of 300 per cubic centimeter, on average, it's not a surprise that some lifeforms have taken advantage of it for communication. Nature doesn't waste a thing.

Antigravity

Many people recall gliding, sliding, and even floating behavior from bigfoot creatures, and other sightings include them effortlessly jumping up into trees. This feature is entirely consistent with EVO activity which, as John Wheeler suggested in the 1950s, creates gravitational fields.

According to Parkhomov, a person close to a small black hole (SBH) would notice the effects:

A person located not far from the flight path of a "typical" SBH will hear a clap rested to the processes in the zone closest to the path and will possibly see small movements of some objects. Most likely, he will not pay any attention to these phenomena, connecting them with any distant gunshot, explosion, or passage of a supersonic aircraft.[120]

In his 1996 interview with Chris Tinsley mentioned above, Martin Fleischmann referred to antigravity as a critical aspect of cold fusion. Gravitational effects were seen by former J. Allen Hynek associate Ted Phillips. In his presentation to the 2009 Ozark Mountain UFO Conference, he mentioned many cases of strange gravitational effects around light orbs, especially at the so-called Marley Woods, Missouri, research site. In one instance, light balls appeared to cause a heavy picnic table to grind around on a cement surface, causing a vibrating sound.

Glowing Eyes

Another common feature of cryptids and bigfoot, in particular, are glowing eyes. One witness said the creature had "eyes that light up like light bulbs."

Eyeglow is different from eyeshine or eyes that reflect light like a deer would. These are actual reports of eyes that emit light, often red, though other colors are seen, such as green, blue, or yellow.[121] Sometimes the eye glow seems to change color. To me, this is a clear indication of some fusion reaction going on. This eyeglow isn't a dull phosphorescent glow seen in some sea creatures like pyrosomes but light that is bright enough to light up a trail.

In Stan Gordon's book *Silent Invasion*, about a wave of UFO and Bigfoot sightings in Pennsylvania in 1973, one of the witnesses describes the human-apelike creatures as having eyes like "balls of fire."[122]

One of the processes in nature that produces a slight glow is scintillation: surfaces that are bombarded by heavy particles emit light. One example is in night vision equipment. Does bigfoot have "natural night vision" built into their visual systems?

A witness in Chile said that she "stared into the creature's eyes, which seemed to emit a fiery beam of light. She felt an electrical discharge . . ."[123]

If cryptids possess a natural cold fusion process in their bodies, perhaps through oxyhydrogen gas (HHO gas) or arterial hydrodynamic compression, it would give them a constant source of scintillation-capable particles. People say the creature's eyes look like dull headlights casting light on the forest ground, so perhaps this is what's going on?

Another interesting related scientific principle related to this is the photoelectric effect discovered by Albert Einstein. As electrons accumulate on a surface of a substance, they will reemit this energy as photons, packets of light. So we can infer that if bigfoots emit light through their eyes in the pitch dark, they also have an internal source of free electrons; in essence, they are electric creatures.

Gliding and Sliding Motions

A witness hiking a 30-mile trail in the Big Cyprus National Preserve in Florida said he saw a bigfoot move oddly. "It's like it floated around the tree."[124]

A former tennis coach said of his sighting at night in central Texas: "This thing was enormous and moved more swiftly and smoothly than a big cat . . . this thing moved unlike anything I have ever witnessed, tame or wild."[125]

A British visitor to the Sea Otter Refuge near Caramel Heights, California, named Claire, reported seeing an adult male, two females, and some juveniles come out towards the beach on all fours. They had a particular "side to side" motion similar to a lizard or gecko. She observed the creatures for a while, gathering seaweed in the water. She was spotted by the male who, after some conversation with one of the females, charged Claire, who passed out from fright. When she later came out of her coma, she found she had been dragged to her car. When asked how fast the creature charged her, she replied: "It wasn't 0 to 60, it was full-on right away."[126]

A camper at Index, Washington, reported seeing a giant shadow glide over a trail behind her trailer before encountering a large creature right next to the vehicle. She wasn't sure if it actually glided or just moved so quickly that it looked like it was gliding. And yet the ground also seemed to shake as the creature moved, first on two legs and then crouching down on all four. "With every step it took, you could feel a thumping vibration coming from the ground."[127]

In another case in rural Maryland, a bigfoot-type creature climbed up a fence surrounding a tennis court in someone's backyard. "It then hopped down from the fence so effortlessly . . . it was so interesting how it didn't make any kind of thud when it landed on the ground . . . (not) even the most skilled athlete on the planet could do that."[128]

Even when the creature can't be seen, when someone is in a tent, for example, the vocal source of a bigfoot can seem to move as if it's gliding around. "There was something about it that was so steady, almost as if whoever was responsible was simply floating from one position of the campsite to another."[129]

One of the most exciting features of cryptids is "Predator-like" transparency (from the 1987 movie of the same name). Witnesses describe something that looks like "Saran Wrap" moving through the forest. In one case, a police officer said he saw a transparent shape move in front of his car that eventually became more solid and took the form of a bigfoot. (See D. Paulides discuss this here: https://youtu.be/YN_m38y3zbI)

Invisibility

The Yellowstone thru-hiker previously mentioned said the following: "It was the strangest thing, like I'd been passed by a ghost, something invisible but with enough weight to make noise as it passed by."[130]

Cindy, previously mentioned above, said, about the creatures near her house at the base of the Blue Ridge Mountains in Virginia: "It should be right in front of me, and I can't see it; I never saw anything. I can't see anything.   It's   just   weird."[131] (https://youtu.be/YAqoW_3F8eM)

She said that she would repeatedly go out right after hearing banging sounds in an attempt to see them but never did. Cindy also mentioned sounds like a bulldozer going through the forest but never saw anything. These "bulldozer from hell" sounds are common to bigfoot sightings.

Similarly, Ron Morehead described strange sounds at the Sierra camp. In one case, metallic clanging sounds near their campsite, like things were being completely trashed, and car doors slammed at other times. But they could never see what caused these sounds. During an interview with me, Ron said that the creatures should have cast a shadow on their group's wooden shelter, which had cracks between the tree trunks, but they never saw anything. Similarly, with pulsating, tuning fork sounds right over their camp.

A scientist in Illinois was parked with his car windows open, playing bigfoot sounds from his car speakers which they hoped would attract the creature. Other researchers were in the woods ahead of him. He heard a car pull up behind him, engine sounds, wheels on gravel, and a car door slamming shut. But when he looked around, no other vehicles were in the parking lot.[132]

Bigfoot can disappear suddenly. Witnesses observing a bigfoot on their property though a night vision scope saw "a sudden flash and it was gone."[133] Carter Buschardt says he once saw something similar when he was looking at a bigfoot with a night scope: there was a flash and then nothing but a "bigfoot smoke ring."[134]

At the Bailey Bigfoot Conference in 2021, Igor Burtsev described the case of a woman in Russia who saw a bigfoot-type creature in her backyard garden. It seemed to be about 8 to 9 feet tall based on the height of power lines behind the house. She said as it walked towards her, it raised its hand in the air and then disappeared in a "curtain of light" from the direction of head to toe, just a few feet in front of her.

Fig. 35. Bigfoot Researchers Don Monroe and Dr. Igor Burtsev at the Bailey Bigfoot Conference, May 2021 (Photo by Author)

Mike Paterson of the website SasquatchOntario.com said in a YouTube interview in 2021: "It's like they disappear into thin air." (https://youtu.be/yJR8VwXRwOA) In this interview, Paterson says it took him eight months to make contact with a group of these creatures on private property, at the owner's request, in a lake area some 2 1/2 hours north of Toronto. He said they could speak essential English words, have families, and can choose to leave tracks and footprints or not.

Kewaunee Lapseritis says that a father and son came up to him after a conference presentation. They had been hunting in Colorado, and the son said something huge and noisy; it made thudding sounds as it ran, passed him in the forest as a deer ran by. While he could see the deer, the thing chasing it was invisible though it moved air as it passed him as he hid behind a tree. After killing the deer, the thing held it by the hind legs in the air and walked towards him but was still invisible. The son ran away in terror.[135]

While investigating the UK crop circles in 2000, a Canadian researcher told me of the following experiences he had while working for Robert Bigelow's NIDs institute at Skinwalker Ranch in Northern Utah in the late 1990s.

One time, he said, they were in the research trailer, all looking through a night vision camera down onto a road below them on the property. Suddenly, they saw a giant "hole" or tube gradually open above the road. Shortly after that, a very tall, giant, dark creature climbed out of the hole and walked away into the darkness. The hole then collapsed in on itself and disappeared. The researchers who witnessed this were highly unnerved by the event. It meant something, an unknown biped, was lurking out there on the property with them.

On another occasion, video cameras on 15-foot poles were set up to observe the Skinwalker property and were installed throughout the area. One night, all of a sudden, according to Kelleher and Knapp, three of the video cameras died at exactly 8:30 pm. The Canadian researcher told me they could see the wires torn out of one of the remote cameras high up on a pole, and the cameras' output was now gone. Although they could see the power and signal wires being torn off the camera, wildly swinging around, they couldn't see what was doing it. In his words, "it was like the cause was invisible."

In *Hunt for the Skinwalker*, Kelleher and Knapp describe an incident where an impromptu visitor to the ranch was standing in a field meditating, with rancher Sherman present, when something rushed them from the tree line at 50 to 60 mph. It looked like a blur, with heat lines and "pixelated blocks." Sherman later said it looked like the creature from the sci-fi movie Predator.

In another incident the following year, something invisible was seen splitting a herd of cattle, "like the Red Sea." in two parts of the field. While it could not be seen even in the high noon sun, the rancher tracked it with a compass as it created strong, magnetic effects.

A similar-looking entity is mentioned in Paulide's video *Missing 411 The Hunted*. Ellen Maccabee described sitting in a tree stand in Lima, Ohio, while deer hunting when something that looked like the plastic film "Saran Wrap" suddenly moved between the trees. She couldn't account for how much time had gone by either, as she initially thought it was only a few minutes but, in reality, was more like an hour.

And in a video posted on YouTube, Barbara Shupe shows us what came through their video camera after sighting what looked like a small monkey in the woods of Western Washington State. While the witnesses saw a small, monkey-like creature in the brush, the camera only records a blurred and pixelated shape. You can watch it for yourself: https://youtu.be/TE-ijkfY9po.

At Marley Woods, Missouri, Ted Phillips says the owners watched as an entire herd of cattle was herded in a field towards a fence. They could barely make out the outline of a nearly invisible shape that reminded them also of the "Predator look" from the movie. And the herd was so shaken by the event they had to be immediately sold. Later they found ten-foot circular seared burn marks in the same area and a mutilated calf like those that also plagued Skinwalker ranch. Who are these entities that move through forests and ranch fields almost invisibly?

Footprints That Disappear in Trackable Ground

In *Hunt for the Skinwalker*, the authors speak of the giant wolf-like creature that visited the Sherman family at their ranch and tried to take one of their calves. Chasing the animal, after shooting it several times to no effect, they followed the tracks for a mile before finding that the tracks just abruptly disappeared in a muddy open area where tracks should have been visible. Suddenly disappearing tracks have also been described in great detail in *Where the Footprints End*, Volumes I and II.[136] As mentioned above, Navajo Ranger Jonathan Dover said he saw vanishing tracks like this while investigating in the Northern part of the Navajo reservation.

Sudden Fog

It's not entirely uncommon for witnesses to bigfoot, balls of light, or UFOs to drive through a sudden fog. I wrote about this in *Black Swan Ghosts* in the case of British researcher Paul Vigay: as he approached the Silbury Hill area in Wiltshire, UK, a strange incident was playing out around the hill witnessed by Paul and Sonya, who were camping there. Paul described approaching a sudden pea-soup-like fog just before seeing a ball of light approach and move behind his vehicle from a hedgerow on the side of the road. The ball of light closely followed his car for a while down the road. (https://youtu.be/sRG6pDcNDAo)

Sudden fog has been reported around other UFO sightings and also bigfoot encounters. When air cools past its saturation point, condensation causes cloud-like droplets to form. In these cases, it seems like the sudden cooling is associated with the cryptid creatures and UFO technology.

Sudden Feelings of Danger and Apprehension

A barista named Nia in a local tea shop here in Boulder, CO, told me that one time she was walking with her sister and father on the Big South Trail near Rocky Mountain National Park. It was a warm day, so she put her sweatshirt by the river near a boulder field about 5 to 7 minutes into the hike. Her sister put the sweatshirt securely under a large rock down a steep hill near the trailhead; it was now completely hidden near the river. After hiding the sweatshirt by the river, they continued hiking for a few minutes. All of a sudden, Nia felt feelings of panic, anxiety, and growing terror. She became sweaty with fear. The trees started to look "weird, skinny, and tall." She felt like something was watching her and told her sister they needed to get out of there quickly. Nia noticed that the hairs on her neck were standing up. They all continued back down the trail for a bit, and she still felt a growing sense of fear. The feeling kept intensifying, and her sister had the same emotion. On the way back to the parking lot, they returned to find the sister's sweatshirt under the rock near the river. It was nowhere to be found. The sister kept looking by the river, but Nia insisted they return to the car. Upon reaching the still empty parking lot, except for their vehicle, they saw the sweatshirt was now neatly placed on top of a giant 12-foot high or so post. The hood was carefully hanging over the top of the post. They had to hop on top of the car's roof to get the sweatshirt. Even their Dad couldn't reach it and thought the whole thing extremely strange. And yet, there were no other cars or people in the parking lot.

On another occasion, Nia's sister Oceania was camping with her boyfriend near Gross Reservoir, Colorado. They parked at the boat launch, paddled in a canoe to the other side of the reservoir, and set up their tent. They heard strange animal sounds from the cliffs and trees above their tent right after dusk. The sounds were like growling and howling with a weird high pitch they couldn't identify. Oceania started to panic, but the boyfriend insisted it must be a bobcat. Then, they noticed rocks being thrown down at their tent from the cliffs that began as small stones and got bigger and bigger. Strangely enough, the rocks and boulders were only falling right around the tent. The whole incident lasted for about 15 minutes. Though they stayed the entire night, the boyfriend admitted on the drive back that he had no idea what the sounds were and had only said they were ordinary animal sounds to calm Oceania down.

Upon telling the previous story above over lunch to a friend of mine, Lauren, who lives in the Boulder area, a memory came back to her of an experience just outside of Rocky Mountain National Park. She was hiking with a friend just to the South of the Park in 2007. They were only a few feet apart on the hiking trail. Suddenly, a huge rock, about 10 inches in diameter, came flying right between them, horizontally, almost hitting her friend in the head. The stone came so close that her friend fell down. There were no noises to indicate that anyone else was around, and Lauren said that the force of the rock would have been enough to kill someone. Its precision was shocking in that it flew right between them. In Lauren's words: "there's nothing to say because you can't talk about it: it's just so damn weird."

Fig. 36. Photo of Lauren's Friend just Before a Large Rock came Flying Between them on the Trail
(Photo by Lauren Watts)

While mentioning the subject of this book at a dinner party, someone named Bob with a lot of camping experience in Colorado volunteered the following story. He said he had pulled into a campsite in the evening north of Granby, CO. Suddenly, he noticed it was getting hushed, almost too quiet. Even the crickets had stopped chirping. And then he began to feel a sense of panic set in. He had no reason to feel that way; the campsite felt eerie. It kept getting worse until he decided to leave. He never saw anything to explain his feelings, but he told me he "thought he was about to die."

A mountain biker was riding in a forest in Holly, Michigan in 2021 when he noticed something following him in the woods for several miles. "The feeling of dread that occupied this was remarkable. It felt like heavy fog but with a physical weight that permeated the forest. It had literal weight to it. Something way nastier than me was in those woods."[137]

I was talking about this topic with a local server, Lucy, in a Boulder restaurant. She told me she was from Humboldt County in California was very familiar with Sasquatch presence. Even as a child she was told be her parents to stay on the trail when walking in a forest, to avoid the "creatures." And she always had the feeling that her parents were not just talking about normal mammals. And even today, while visiting her parents in a remote part of the county, she says she doesn't go out of the house at night, due to the "weird nighttime feelings" in the area. While she has never seen or heard Sasquatch she felt they definitely had a presence in the area.

Another story I came across while writing this book concerns a man named Lynn from Potlatch, Idaho. He told me that, in the 1980s, he was driving home at night a few miles north of Moscow on route 95 when he began to feel sleepy and decided to pull over onto a graveled area on the side of the road. He was fast asleep in the driver's seat when he heard the sound of crunching gravel made by something on two legs. It slowly circled his truck, and he felt it looking down at him through the windshield though he could never see it. Lynn felt such a sense of intense terror that he started screaming. He had the feeling that whatever was out there was around eight feet tall and menacing. Lynn said that just recounting this story to me made the hair stand up on his arms: "Whatever they are, they're from somewhere else."

Fig. 37. Approximate Location of Lynn's Encounter in the 1980s
(Image ©2022 by Apple Maps)

Transforming Into Inanimate Objects

Ordinary people, hunters, and outdoors enthusiasts have reported bigfoot-type creatures turning into different objects, apparently as disguises. This includes branches, boulders, tree stumps, piles of bark, or even people.[138] In one case, a witness had "sightings of 'bushes' that were not there the day before and are gone the day after the sighting."[139]

And (gulp) it also works in reverse: yes, the tree stumps turn back into bigfoot once people have left the area. No joke. Yes, this sounds strange, but that's what witnesses say they see.

Witness Brain Fog

A long-distance trail hiker with years of military training, walking through Yellowstone on the Continental Divide Trail encountered a bigfoot and said the following: "do know that before all this happened, I was leading a pretty normal life, one that was about as good as one could expect, given all the things we have to deal with. Now I feel like I'm sometimes in a fog."[140]

The witness to the Drake, CO encounter told me she felt as if she had "brain fog" for exactly a day and a half after the incident that drained the battery on her cell phone.
(http://bfro.net/GDB/show_report.asp?id=62929)

Lauren, in Colorado, mentioned above, was visiting Rocky Mountain National Park with a companion and told me the following strange story. She and her friend had started hiking at about 2:30 in the afternoon and were on a hiking trail in the park when they suddenly found themselves back in the parking lot they had started from, only now it was around 4:30 pm. Two hours had elapsed. Neither of them could explain it.

A bigfoot researcher named Kenny Collins at the Bailey Conference in 2021 also relayed the following story. He was observing a juvenile Bigfoot about 30 feet away behind some rocks in an area near Estes Park. The creature was sort of chuckling a bit, Kenny thought. Kenny raised his camera to take a picture, and the next thing he knew, he was back in his truck, which would have been a ten-minute walk away, with the ignition on. Checking his camera, he saw that he hadn't taken any pictures.[141]

So, to put it simply, if bigfoot or any other cryptids can create bunched electron structures from the static in their long hair, the compression of their huge feet on the ground, piezoelectrical effect in their bones, or the vortical action of blood flowing in their cavernous arterial structure, they would be able to create the itonic mesh structure that Matsumoto says is the hallmark of neutron stars and cold fusion processes. These creatures would have unique gravitational abilities due to their ability to harness dark matter energies!

That probably sounds strange, but if you think about the encounters people report, there are often gravitational effects, missing time, and electronic anomalies.

More Field Like, Less Point Like

We're accustomed to seeing life as something purely physical, solid, and well-defined. But the evidence in this book points to a more field-like type of life that is more challenging for us to identify. We're all used to field-like resonance like music, for example. If you've ever been to a memorable music concert, you'll know the power of energetic, vibrational fields. The English physicist Faraday made electromagnetic fields a thing of scientific study. But it's hard for us to imagine that living things can inhabit these fields in addition to physical spaces.

The late physicist William Tiller referred to these fields as "R-space" instead of "D-space."[142]1 I always thought of it as Resonant Space as opposed to Direct Space. It seems to me that cryptids are creatures that occupy these R-spaces as opposed to only D-spaces. They can shift back and forth between these types of space, confounding our human sense of reality.

Now, you've probably experienced this field-like sense of reality when you're dreaming at night, during meditation, or in any similar state. Bill Tiller used to focus on showing that these states have direct, physical impacts that are measurable. For example, he believed he had demonstrated that advanced practitioners of Transcendental Meditation could affect the properties of spaces around them or objects they focused on during meditation.

So let's say that cryptids are beings that have learned how to do the same thing without going to Maharishi University? They can focus resonant energies in the same way your dog can convince you to give them some of your food from the dinner table. Can these cryptids manipulate you energetically, just like your pet cat, dog, or neighborhood squirrels do with food? Would that be so surprising? Sure, it would make them seem paranormal, but no more so than that squirrel staring at you through the window telling you to refill your easily accessible bird feeder. Is that squirrel telepathic or just very good at communicating with you?

Remote Influencing

We're familiar with the government-sponsored remote viewing program, run by the Defense Intelligence Agency in the 1970s and later by the Central Intelligence Agency until 1995. Stanford Research Institute carried out a lot of the research with natural psychics like Ingo Swann and Pat Price. The program had various codenames over the years, including Project Stargate, and intended to create a cadre of psychic spies who could view and acquire valuable information not accessible by other conventional means for the US military and intelligence agencies. (See the documentary *Third Eye Spies* by Russell Targ and Lance Mungia for details about the RV program.)

If you talk with remote viewers from the US program, you'll find that there was also research in psychokinesis and "remote influencing": the ability to affect things and people at a distance.

Princeton University even had the PEAR Labs, Princeton Engineering Anomalies Research Lab. Twenty years of Lab research showed that the average person could, through mental intention, affect a random number generator about 2 to 3 times every 10,000 cycles of random number generation. Bob Jahn and Brenda Dunn spent two decades showing this is true. When I asked York Dobyns, their lab scientist whose job was to look for flaws or holes in their experiments, if any of these could have had a pronounced "common sense" explanation, one that the lab might have overlooked, he said "no." It's a natural, psychic effect.

US Government Monitors 1970s Soviet PK Experiment

I further confirmed the existence of PK when talking with a former Pentagon official who told me that the US had monitored a Soviet PK experiment in 1976. One thousand miles from Moscow, the PK sender had bent a spoon there on command. Thirty members of the US intelligence community were monitoring the event when it happened, and it's a historical fact. Yet how many people have ever heard of this event outside of that room of the thirty intelligence officers? (You've just read about this event so now there's one more!)

So if you're surprised that the US government has documented that PK exists, is it any more surprising that a type of life exists on Earth that can naturally do similar things, and you haven't been told about it?

Agitation of Dogs and Animals

The owners of Skinwalker Ranch often noticed that their dogs and livestock were agitated by things the Shermans couldn't see: invisible entities causing these animals to chase them or run away in fear.

Dogs, in particular, are known to avoid or even cower in fear of bigfoot creatures. You'll read about this again no matter which witness you hear from. You can see an example of this for yourself in the following video taken in Minnesota, where a Jack Russell dog, "Riff," first pursues a Bigfoot and then runs away safely, barking at the creature from a distance. (https://youtu.be/NeIq3Og0XRo)

ET Technology that Interacts Directly with the Quantum Vacuum

Several years ago, I met an engineer at a science conference during a dinner buffet after the first day's lectures. The subject of UFOs came up, and this engineer volunteered that he had once been asked, by "someone," to examine a piece of slightly curved wreckage about 3-foot across. It was made of nanotechnology and extremely thin yet hard. He told those of us at the dinner table that based on the curvature; he estimated that craft it came from at about 80 feet across.

Over the next few days, I asked him more questions about the artifact. He was convinced it was about 1,000 years ahead of our technology, and tests showed it was made of isotopes not naturally occurring on Earth but from somewhere else in the galaxy. He was confident it was extraterrestrial technology, and so was the agency which possessed it. He was asked to figure out how it worked, and he told me it wasn't possible with our level of scientific understanding though it had something to do with "quantum vacuum engineering." This individual never wanted to talk with me about it again; no interviews, no YouTube live streams.

So, the question is, how many people are out there like this, highly qualified professionals, who've seen what they believe to be clear evidence of ET technology and won't go public for whatever reason? And if experts like this won't talk about ET stuff publicly, how likely are we to hear about anything related to cryptids, which some may find equally disruptive or disturbing?

My point is that stigma, fear of ridicule, and possible government sanctions on those who are privy to these secrets might have squashed any discussion so far, which is why we don't know much about these subjects, real as they are.

And another distinct possibility is that apart from the fear of recalling these encounters, we may be having them and forgetting about them. How many people experienced "escaped gorillas" or "monkeys" in the woods and then forgot about it? Are we dealing with a species that can manipulate human minds so that we've lost recall of our encounters with them, like collective amnesia? Are we the ones living in a bubble of unreality because we forget experiences from "outside the box"?

Similarity between UFO, Bigfoot and Other Phenomena

There are so many overlaps between these different experiences that we're probably dealing with the same fundamental resonant processes. We're talking about systems of energy that are autonomous, self-organizing, powerful, and highly connected to nature. Both technological and natural at the same time. They're all tapping into the same level of nature that creates and destroys matter and interacts with the universe's dark matter. And the by-product of those states of matter for ordinary mortals who happen to be around is time loss, confusion, brain fog, and space-time blending. When we look at it this way, it doesn't seem so strange all of sudden, so scary. And perhaps that's the first step in having a more productive relationship with the dark matter universe and its residents.

Chapter 10—Cryptids and Forward-Facing Resonance

"The recordings we made in the Sierra Nevada Mountains command all that classical science can muster, yet must also include open-mindedness. Scientists should consider all the reports they have at their disposal; not discard them because they don t fit into their discipline, or their paradigm."—

Ron Morehead and Thomas Powell. *Voices in the Wilderness: A True Story*

This section is more speculative, and I'm including it here to stimulate more discussion on the subject. In the previous chapters, I suggested that cryptids can absorb and generate active neutrinos in the same way cold fusion reactors do. To sustain an energetic chain-reaction, these creatures need a resonance feedback system. And this resonance sustaining process would create a low level of charge clusters: the same charge clusters we find in ball lightning and cold fusion reactions. In this sense, perhaps the bigfoot howls and screams are not just for show but are a type of energetically active frequency that sustains these reactions. In fact, the sounds kind of reminds me of the way Robert Plant sounded at a Led Zeppelin concert I saw in New York City in 1977. Sure, the sounds he made were musical, but they also created a crowd-pleasing vibe that went beyond the original sound you heard on the record. Could superstar musicians be aware of the secrets and powers of resonance?

Wood Knocking and Tapping Sounds

So perhaps the sounds that cryptids are known to make, tapping and knocking and shrieking, are not just to scare people away but also serve as a resonant feedback frequency?

If you think I'm just throwing this idea out there, I have some evidence: psychokinesis. Sometimes abbreviated as PK, psychokinesis is the ability to physically influence matter using mental or biological energy.

Real PK

While teaching remote viewing in Japan, one of the people in the class, a cancer surgeon, took me to see a genuine psychokinesis practitioner. He could do lots of stuff. At the end of the demonstration, he asked me to hold out my arm: he ran his hand over it from a distance of about a foot, and I could feel an electric type feeling up and down my arm!

Fig. 38. Soda Bottle Twisted and Melted by Psychokinesis Practitioner in
Japan
(Photo by Author)

So perhaps this is a natural ability that most of us don't think we have, but cryptids know how to use very well.

How Long Does It Take for Us to Understand Reality?

At the beginning of this book, you might have thought that the subjects discussed here are "paranormal" or "fringe" topics. Yet, as we've seen, the US government has repeatedly investigated these topics in classified and unclassified forms. And at least two different formers members of the intelligence community, James Lacatski and John Ramirez, have told us that there is an invisible world around us that produces cryptids, UFOs, orbs, and other non-ordinary phenomena. Thousands of people have

184 Dark Matter Monsters

witnessed these phenomena, and now we know that they have a reality beyond our ordinary consensus reality but are right next to us nonetheless.

We've seen that some of these non-ordinary effects are already well-known in scientists' labs, at Lockheed Martin, for example, studying coherent matter phenomena: ball lightning, invisibility, transmutation, and teleportation.

And you may think it's a little off the wall for me to suggest that cryptid creatures like bigfoot have anything to do with dark matter. If you disagree with me, I challenge you to come up with a better explanation of why these creatures, and others like them, are connected to the spontaneous magnetization of materials, ball lightning, space-time distortions, brain fog in witnesses, and drained batteries. It just doesn't seem like these artifacts could be created by any conventional phenomena.

And there is an even bigger question: How long does it take for us as individuals to understand such a reality? It took me over half a century to know what I've described in this book. A few years ago, I might not have even been open to the topics of cryptids and orbs as something to be taken seriously. Yet now I do. So, if it took an open-minded person like myself decades to start investigating this topic, how far off from reality is our day-to-day consensus reality? The one we hear on TV, on the news, from our friends?

And to me, this might be the most important topic of all: our general sense of reality is far too limited.

Chapter 11—Our Fractal Universe

Fractals are self-similar objects that look like things in nature, trees, clouds, mountains, our lungs, and hair. They are inherently wiggly and lumpy. Also, the shape of the rhythms of our hearts and brains are fractals, opposite linear shapes like lines and boxes. Although associated with mathematician Benoit Mandelbrot, the "father of fractals," they were suggested by physicists like Paul Dirac. He noticed similarities in the sizes of cosmological objects like galaxies and the widths of atoms, and these are known as Dirac's "Law of Large Numbers."

Fractals show us that in nature, the microcosm is like the macrocosm and that even things of different sizes can share more general invariant qualities like similar frequencies and resonance. We can ascribe a fractal dimension to objects' surfaces, which describes their complexity, wiggliness, and lumpiness.

The higher the fractal dimension, the more complex

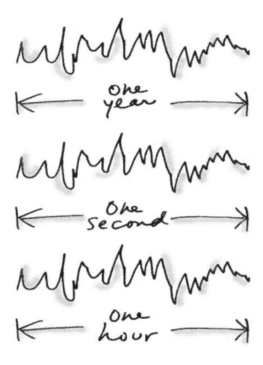

Fig. 39. Self-Similarity at Different Time Scales
(Drawing ©2002 by Ira G. Liss)

and dense their surfaces. For example, a straighter coastline has a lower fractal dimension than one with lots of crags and bends, and the one with more detail, inlets, and variation would have a higher dimension.

Self-similarity means that the closer you look, the more detail you'll see. The object won't resolve to a

Fig. 40. Abstract Fractal Shape: each Smaller Level is Similar to the Larger Ones. This Shape Appears key to Tapping Quantum Vacuum Energy. (Image by Sharon Apted, CC0 1.0)

simple line. So, things with a higher fractal number have continuity from a small to a large scale because the density of detail at any level is the same.

For example, while working for IBM, Mandelbrot discovered that line noise in telephone signals is fractal: there's the same amount of signal variation over a minute, an hour, or a day. The shape of the signal looks the same at any time interval.

One of the fractal patterns that are common in nature is called the 1/F spectra, which we can relate to music: there is more variation in the high notes than low   notes.

Fig. 41. Music is Fractal
(Drawing by ©2002 by Ira G. Liss)

Russian nuclear scientist Dr. Alexander Parkhomov found this pattern throughout cosmological and nuclear processes at an atomic level. He calls it "flicker noise" because of its subtle nature. He explains how flicker noise triggers snow avalanches, earthquakes, and rock falls. Not necessarily the loudest sounds, but the ones that repeat at a low signal strength. And it is this flicker noise that Parkhomov finds in cold fusion processes. This shows us that cold fusion reactions are similar to those at a stellar level: they're like miniature suns.

Parkhomov found that lunar-terrestrial interactions and solar-terrestrial interactions affect things like Earth's nuclear decay rates. So these are cosmic neutrino energies focused or lensed by the positions of the Moon and Earth in relation to the Milky Way galaxy. Something like a celestial aether supposedly disproved by the famous Michaelson-Morley experiments over a century ago.

Now, if you're having trouble visualizing flicker noise, it's the same thing as that warning you see on your Xbox when you start it up. The warning notice says that the flickering lights on some video games could trigger epileptic seizures in some people. That, my friends, is flicker noise in a nutshell: tiny, seemingly insignificant pulses of energy leading to a significant collective outcome in the brain of an epileptic person.

Avalanche-Like Energy Releases

Things that are shaped like fractals, as you would expect, don't obey linear laws of cause and effect. Not only are they non-linear, but energy can be released from them in avalanche-like ways, just Parkhomov describes. This is the result of many interacting parts all equally influencing each other. And the interactivity of relic neutrinos is like flicker noise because there are lots of them all around, and they constantly interact with each other and everything they come in contact with.

Russian scientist Simon Schnoll has even proposed that ALL chemical, biological, and physical processes correlate with each other because of this principle. This is due to "cosmophysical factors in random processes." If everything is affected by and entangled with these relic neutrinos, then there is nothing random in our universe. Everything is interrelated in some way! What a concept.

Fractal Energy Clusters

Another aspect of fractals is that the EVOs we've been talking about are fractal objects composed of many nested, interacting, rotating energy vortexes and rings. Each ring makes up a larger ring of a large-scale object up to a few feet. (Robert Greenyer of the non-profit Martin Fleischmann Memorial Project has done a great job explaining this, and

I refer you to his YouTube videos.[143]) One of Kenneth R. Shoulders EVO experiments shows a fractal structure.

But the main point for us is that the basis of our

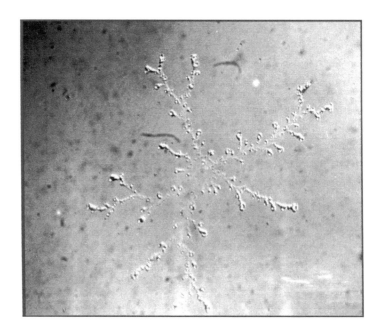

Fig. 42. EVO Swarm Showing Fractal Structures
(Photo ©2004 by Kenneth R. Shoulders)

universe is that everything is spinning, rotating in a vortex-like way. It's called "helicity" in modern parlance and suggests that the basis of life is spiraling motion. And any creatures that incorporate this somehow in their physiology would create energy in exciting and novel ways. We humans and other animals already include this principle in the shapes of inner ears in the cochlea, our hearts' forms, and the spiral flow of blood in arteries.

And so, from this point of view, the most natural shapes in the world would be spirals, not lines. And we would expect chemical and physical processes at the micro-level to also show spiral patterns. We see precisely this when we look at the shapes of cold fusion and LENR processes; it's called "strange tracks" and is a characteristic of the radiation patterns of energy in these reactions. Spiral energy paths are boring twisted holes through solid surfaces.

By firing simultaneously two or more plasmoids across a magnetic field it has been possible to produce cooperative phenomena which, in geometrical form, suggest the simulation of the production of spiral galaxies and astronomical barred spirals. There is hence some promise that it will be possible to study these astronomical processes in the laboratory. — (Bostick, 1957)

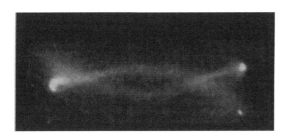

Fig. 43. Spiraling Test-Tube Plasmoids
(Photo ©1980 by Bostick and Nardi)

Fig. 44. Spiraling Electron Clusters (Photo ©2004 by Kenneth R. Shoulders)

Fig. 45. Galaxy-Shaped "Test-Tube" Plasmoid (Photo ©1956 by Winston Bostick)

The idea that the spiral shape of galaxies is caused by the same forces in a test tube is the essence of fractals and suggests that the same fundamental forces in the universe produce structures and life at hugely different scales.

Electromagnetic Phantoms and the Fractal Structure of Space-Time

As of the writing of this book, a scientific paper emerged from previously classified research in the Soviet Union in the 1980s. It is called the "The Bagel Game," and the author, V.E. Zhvirblis, explains how he was privy to a secret Soviet electromagnetic experiment. He was invited to a facility to watch so-called "electromagnetic phantoms": coiled, self-similar toroids that produced self-sustaining, "closed" magnetic flux loops. In contrast, to open flux loops that we're used to in everyday technology, these closed loops do not dissipate but concentrate energy instead. Zhvirblis explains how even when this device was turned off, it still generated a steady electrical flow for an astounding 2 days! And when the magnetic toroid was removed from the table-top, the vibrant glow of the flux loops stayed in the same place on the table surface. It could even be swept away with one's hand. While not explicitly mentioning ball lightning, it's clear that this research, based on a fractal magnetic structure, created anomalous energy flows that exist on an entirely different scientific basis, though one compatible with Maxwell's electromagnetic equations, as explained by the author's friend and mathematician, N. E. Nevessky. Both authors conclude that this self-similar, fractal, magnetic structure directly taps into the energy of the quantum vacuum. This is another critical milestone connecting coherent matter to fractal structures. In fact, these authors conclude that this is the only shape that will completely fill space-time.

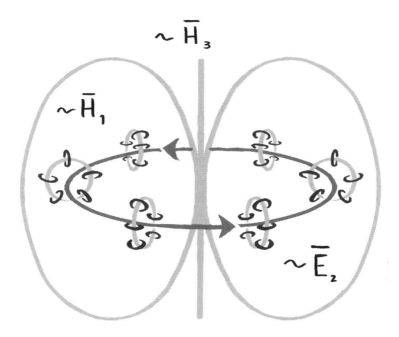

Fig. 46. Fractal Maxwellian Electromagnetic Field Structure
Discovered by Zhvirblis and Nevessky in the 1990s
(Drawing ©2022 by Eva Giddings)

Chapter 12—Energy Generating Behavior, Chain Reactions, and the Biology of Coherent Matter Lifeforms

"Don't tell nature what it is; let nature speak to you"
Francesco Piantelli, January 2015

I'd suggest that the best way to understand our interactions with coherent matter is to look in nature to see where we may find charge clusters already at work. Then we might be able to see where this is happening in familiar animals and extend this understanding to cryptids.

Japanese nuclear researcher Takaaki Matsumoto suggests that what we see going in cold fusion reactions is the same process as in stars, a type of condensed matter reaction. Its nature's way of generating energy by converting hydrogen, the most abundant element in the universe, into other members of the periodic table and releasing lots of energy in the process. From this perspective, cold fusion and ball lightning produced in a lab are just a small-scale version of what's happening at cosmic levels.

According to Matsumoto, all cold fusion processes produce dark matter as part and parcel of these reactions—technically called "inverse beta decay." The high energies involved in cold fusion produce so-called "cold neutrinos," as will any high-temperature reaction above 1000 Centigrade. Cold neutrinos, slow-moving compared to solar neutrinos, as slow as 10 kilometers per hour in our solar system, are similar to the relic neutrinos from the Cosmic Background Radiation in size and wavelength frequency. We can, unofficially, call both types of neutrinos Active Neutrinos as they interact with groups of atoms and biological material, unlike their solar neutrino relatives. Scientists at CERN in Switzerland and some at NASA contend that these types of neutrinos are a significant component of dark matter.

> Extraordinary phenomena have been observed in the natural environment so far. Many of them are found to be associated with the electrical discharge, but left unexplained. However, they also might be made clear by similar mechanisms to cold fusion. For example, *tiny ball lightnings* [my emphasis] were observed during a discharging cold fusion experiment.[146]

From this perspective, cryptids could be Earthly occupants who have learned to adapt this cosmological process to their particular biological and chemical processes. And if Matsumoto is correct, they are also GENERATING DARK MATTER. That's right, the natural cold neutrinos emitted by biological and nuclear interactions have the same fundamental properties and wavelengths as those from the cosmic background. Just because we don't wholly understand coherent matter, or might be rediscovering it nowadays, doesn't mean that some other creatures aren't already using it in their metabolic life.

If we look at a typical bigfoot-type creature, we can see features of their physiology that would support charge cluster and neutrino generating activity. Their vast size would mean that just walking around and pounding the ground would create cavitation forces known to generate charge clusters.

Secondly, their larger body would have a larger arterial structure than ours. This fluid capacity would allow for hydrodynamic vortex action in the arteries and veins and also be a source of charge cluster generation.

Thirdly, their abundant, often lengthy, hair would be a source of electrostatic charges. Ken Shoulders identified cat's hair, amber, and bee wax as natural materials that the Egyptians might have used to generate charge clusters. The point is that these are part of nature, not something that had to be invented along with modern semiconductors.

We can speculate that if cryptids are harnessing dark matter in their biology, it suggests that something in their bodies allows them to compress water and hydrogen clusters. We can imagine that they might use minerals to do this or a particular mineral-lined organ or surface that can accomplish what palladium seems to achieve in a cold fusion reaction process. We would have natural cold fusion creatures and the associated dark matter products combined with cavitation.

Many witnesses describe an odd, energetic feeling shortly before their encounters with these creatures. Is it just some survival instinct that kicks in? Or is it because of their proximity to these dark matter components and time-dilating and gravity-distorting effects?

Cryptids might tap into a chain reaction of charge clusters that absorb neutrinos from the environment, generate charge clusters from their bodily motion and interaction with the Earth, and then convert this energy to dark matter, as Matsumoto argues in cold fusion/LENR reactions.

Any creature that could create such dark matter would be able to produce all types of seemingly paranormal phenomena mentioned in Chapter 4: balls of light, static charges, cloaking, and even self-generated gravitic forces. It's no wonder that humans who encounter these creatures are perpetually baffled by their ability to glide, float, and short out batteries and electronic equipment.

But there's more to it than that. Since dark matter is only detectable gravitationally, depending on how cryptids use the dark stuff, these creatures would be able to be in the same physical space as we are without being visible! You might experience some of the other coherent matter effects mentioned above, but you wouldn't see who or what was producing it.

In short, these sorts of creatures would excel at moving quickly and staying hidden. And when you did interact with them, you would experience a range of quantum effects that we've shown are the outcome of compressed and condensed matter: time-space dilation, sudden cold, mental confusion, memory loss, and strange luminous phenomena like orbs.

These are many characteristics of what we often call "paranormal phenomena." Only they're not "paranormal": just the strange outcomes of some process that allows these cryptids to condense and compress matter until it becomes coherent.

Advantages of Dark Matter Monsters over Humans

Immediately we can see that any organism using dark matter as an energy source would have some serious advantages over ordinary humans, like cloaking and anti-gravity abilities. It explains why some Sasquatch can run as fast as cars going 45 mph or more; they can jump up into trees; glide down from fences and over the ground, and around balls of light. These abilities are related to Ken Shoulder's Exotic Vacuum Objects (EVOs). Even Winston H. Bostick in the 1950s noted the anti-gravitational effects of plasma clusters. Anti-gravitational results aren't surprising given the energy density of ball lightning is as high as 20,000J/cm3, ten times as high as the explosive TNT![147]

In 2010, the CERN laboratory in Switzerland stated the relic neutrino was the most likely candidate for dark matter.[148] Even with new ideas about "teleparallel gravity," something Einstein briefly looked into, attempting to replace the whole concept of dark matter, it doesn't affect the status of the relic neutrino as a fundamental yet under-appreciated particle.[149] Whatever the source of cryptids' remarkable abilities, it's something to consider the next time you find yourself in the great outdoors.

Do Cryptids Exist in Parallel Realities?

Previously in this book, we looked at the idea of mirror neutrons creating parallel Earths. Do cryptids inhabit these other worlds, and is that where they reside? It's a big question, but the reality is that scientists have been debating these possibilities for a long time.

Around one hundred years ago, a group of scientists invented Quantum Mechanics by resolving paradoxes in classical physics as Einstein and Planck did with the Black Body Problem. Yet the question of how a wave-like description of reality was consistent with that of tiny, equally-charged energy packets called particles was unresolved, even to this day. The Schrödinger Wave Function describes reality in terms of probability waves where particles are likely to be found. Yet the Wave Function also describes worlds and the behavior of particles that we never see. Where do they go?

One way out of this problem was to create the idea of "wave function collapse," suggested by John Von Neumann. In his view, the wave function collapsed as soon as a human observer observed the system. But this created another issue: where do all the collapsed wave functions go? If probabilities describe reality, why does our world appear so solid, defined, and consistent? This idea became known as the "Preferred Basis Problem."

Suppose objects can be described differently, with different colors, shapes, or patterns. Why do they appear so specifically instead of looking vague, wavy, and ghostly? In theory, with the idea of wave collapse, trees look green to us because all the trees that look purple or pink disappeared in a supposed "wave function collapse."

In the 1950s, a graduate student at Princeton University, Hugh Everett III, proposed another solution: that all possibilities exist for any object or group of things. Still, we only perceive a fraction of them because we are also quantum objects undergoing continuous evolution. There is nothing to collapse. Instead, we're just observing one path of quantum evolution that we're entangled with. But the other paths still exist, even if we do not perceive them. This idea became known as the Many Worlds Interpretation. The observer is NOT separated from what they are observing. It's one big wave function, and we're part of it, too, entangled with everything we perceive. And there are other versions of us perceiving reality differently.

And an even newer interpretation of the Many Worlds is an idea created recently by Howard Wiseman, Dirk-Andre Decker, and Michael Hall.[148] They see no need for a Quantum Wave Function at all. It's called the Many Interacting Worlds model. Supporters of this viewpoint have shown that parallel realities interacting with each other, ever so slightly, reproduce the Quantum Wave Function almost exactly (down to 7 or 8 decimal places). As *New Scientist* magazine describes the MIW perspective:

"Quantum weirdness is a sign of many ordinary but invisible universes jostling to share the same space as ours."[149]

As all these universes interact, it creates what appears to us as a quantum wave function and "ghostly" phenomena like quantum tunneling and the double-slit experiment where particles appear wave-like and particle-like simultaneously. So from this point of view, quantum mechanics is the product of a multiverse of interacting parallel realities.

And this idea seriously opens the door for weird things to show up in our reality. As Howard Wiseman said in an interview with New Scientist magazine: "It's not part of our theory, but the idea of [human] interactions with other universes is no longer pure fantasy."

Kenneth R. Shoulders' observation reinforces this point of view that "black-mode" electron charge clusters, EVOS, seem to disappear from our world into a different universe: "A physical matter leak occurs between our Universe and another still unexplored one." Shoulders is saying that ball lightning is a gateway to another dimension that we can't directly perceive.

No matter which version of the multiverse you adhere to, the implications are that there might be invisible realities all around us that exist separately from ours, but not entirely. And perhaps this is where cryptids exist: in a parallel reality that interacts with ours from time to time. And coherent matter is the bridge that allows them to travel between parallel worlds. At least this is one possibility.

How to Prepare Yourself

First, it's essential to get over societal prejudice about "non-ordinary" lifeforms, terrestrial or otherwise, and accept the existence of these creatures. Secondly, be aware of your surroundings and maintain your situational awareness. Trust your intuition and pay attention when your internal alarm bells start ringing. Thirdly, learn as much as you can. The most important thing is knowing more about nature, how it works, and how you are connected. Because in many ways, these creatures are much closer to nature than we are, and their powers are entirely from natural sources, not technological.

Sometimes they look like "Saran Wrap" moving through the trees. Other times, they appear as flesh and blood creatures or may even be invisible. They may appear as something you've never even seen before. If you pay attention to your gut feelings, you're more likely to be aware of them in advance.

Chapter 13—It's the Things You Can't See That Matter the Most

"This is a tangible manifestation of something we don't understand."—John Ramirez, CIA Signals Intelligence Officer (retired)[153]

"I think Hell has not a clue as to the fury of a bunch of electrons suddenly unleashed."—Kenneth R. Shoulders[154]

Our mechanistic worldview that most of us have grown up with trains us to pay attention to large, linear interactions. Like in an automobile, all the parts have a specific function; if one breaks, you replace it. The accelerator is a linear mechanism: the harder you push, the faster the car goes. And there's an onboard diagnostic computer that sends you error codes (in newer cars).

Suppose you think about a conventional gas auto engine. The engine is made of parts we can physically see and operates on principles that are easy to understand: exploding fuels like gasoline that creates pressure and pushes the metal cylinders forward; how the engine converts rotational energy into power that moves the transmission; and a how a clutch converts that energy into different speeds. We can relate to all these mechanical processes because they're linear and proportional.

However, biological and chemical systems are not necessarily like this. They have more nuanced components in a fractal arrangement so that all the parts contribute to a whole that is more than the sum. As we mentioned with Parkhomov, the elements interact with each other in a complex fashion to create flicker noise. And outcomes from interventions in such processes are harder to predict.

For example, researchers have recently discovered our microbiome with trillions of tiny cells that outnumber our cells on the order of 10 to 1. We have thousands of these organisms in our digestive tracts, in our mouths, and on our skin, and the vast majority of them have never been identified and don't have names.

These tiny organisms have recently been subject to a lot of attention because they affect our moods, nutrition, and disease. There is even speculation that there is a direct connection between the macrobiotic organisms in our gut and brain. So there is a belief that our brain and moods are influenced by teensy weensy cells in ways that science is just beginning to learn about. Other studies have linked the microorganisms to obesity and still others to diabetes, one of the top ten leading causes of death worldwide.

Similarly, scientists are beginning to look at the effect of pesticides and biocides on soil microbiota. There has been a lot of research on the impact of pesticides on insects and plants. However, not much work has gone into investigating the effects of these chemicals on soil mainly composed of living microorganisms.

Another example is microplastics. Current estimates are that there will be more microplastics in our oceans by weight by 2050 than biological organisms, including all plants, corals, and animals. Microplastics don't only affect ocean-going animals and marine life that eat them. These plastics break down into ever tinier pieces and affect any number of creatures and cellular components in strange ways. Microscopic organisms attach themselves to these little pieces of plastic. But because these plastics turn into ever smaller pieces, eventually into chemical elements, scientists don't understand the long-term planetary consequences.

Tiny Neutrinos Create Big Effects

So it's no surprise scientists that Matsumoto has found that tiny clusters of hydrogen atoms, even regular water, and their interactions with even smaller relic neutrinos are the foundation of the cold fusion process. So while mainstream science has been preoccupied with hot fusion with its billion dollar research budgets and huge physical facilities, cold fusion can be demonstrated for about $30 using commonly available ultrasonic cleaners you can easily find online, plus water and some aluminum foil. You'll need an electron microscope to see the micro cluster artifacts produced by your experiment. And that's the point: The effects that lead to such outcomes happen on a small scale, and we haven't paid much attention to them.

If we're beginning to learn about our microbiome, is it any surprise that tiny atomic interactions involving neutrinos have also escaped our attention? Nature operates at macro-scales and micro-scales, and our modern society, by and large, has been preoccupied with the largest of things like cell phones, spark plugs, and laptops while ignoring the quantum processes that make these possible in the first place.

Biological processes are probably intertwined with many quantum and cosmic phenomena that we've barely investigated. One military-trained remote viewer once told me: "I don't need to know how my car works to drive it, and I want remote viewing results, not an understanding of physics behind it." This attitude is understandable from a military mindset, but science has to have some theory behind it, or we'll come to a standstill in our knowledge our how nature works.

Similarly with bigfoot and cryptids: their extraordinary abilities may stem from microscopic nuclear, chemical and biological properties discovered long ago but only recently understood and tested.

Hitchhiker Effect: Contagion or Resonance?

One of the main ideas to emerge from the AAWSAP research at Skinwalker Ranch is the notion that anomalous living entities can "follow" you home from "haunted" locations. It's almost as if something can attach itself to you while you're there, return with you to your home back in the "real world," and then spread throughout your neighborhood, as in the case the researcher named Axelrod mentioned by Lakatski. This condition has been called the "Hitchhiker Effect". In a recent article, Kelleher suggests that it's a contagion like a medical disease. It's almost like picking up some "bad juju" at a haunted location, and then it spreads to everyone you know like a virus.[155]

First, it's important to note that the contagion model has been applied to many network phenomena beyond direct infection from one person to another. For example, a Harvard study from 2007 found that obesity could be explained with a contagion model. There are social networks of obese people, some of whom don't even see each other in person but communicate by phone or online. But no one I know is suggesting that a virtual or physical virus particle spreads obesity. So this is a case of applying a math model to as many different phenomena as possible when we might be served better by alternative interpretations. The medical contagion "threat" model might be socially acceptable to mainstream scientists and those in the defense establishment. But it doesn't get to the root cause of the phenomenon.

If "weird" phenomena spread by contagion, like a disease, almost everyone should have encountered dogman, giant birds, and bigfoot in their backyards by now. But they haven't. Things like COVID spread by contagion: cryptid   encounters   seem   far   less predictable.

Secondly,   the   hitchhiker   idea   isn't   a   new observation. People who experience plasmas and self-organized light phenomena are known to have novel and seemingly paranormal experiences around their homes and in their lives. In a case mentioned by author Andrew Collins, the Day family was driving in a car at night in 1977 on the outskirts of London near Aveley when they saw an "electric-blue light" pass over them. They then encountered a luminous green mist on the road. They noticed a tingling sensation in their hair. The car radio went out and started to smoke, the lights dimmed, and the engine died. Three hours later, they were half a mile further down the road without any memories of what happened. The car had restarted on its own, and they all felt groggy and tired. They never talked about it after that. Yet, over the following months and years, they all began to notice strange happenings in their home, poltergeist activity, and bursts of light. But that isn't all that occurred. They all started noticing new psychic abilities. Both parents gave up alcohol and cigarettes (John Day had been a heavy chain smoker). They developed artistic talents and interests in new fields. John's wife, Sue, became a nurse serving in the first Gulf War in 1991, and he developed an interest in the environment and went to college to learn art and sculpture.[156]

The point here is that this couple transformed their experience into something positive. They became new people. I'd suggest that rather than something "attaching" itself to this "family in the mist," instead, they experienced a multidimensional energy form that night, which changed them in definite ways. We saw earlier in this book that ball lightning, by its intense gravitational and magnetic effects, creates chemical transmutation in materials it encounters. But there's another possibility: that ball lightning creates a multidimensional binding effect: a shift in their physiological resonance, which would explain why people who come into contact with this luminous object later experience new phenomena and identities around them. Nothing is attaching itself to these witnesses. They're also likely generating more cold neutrinos, as mentioned earlier. So they've changed in ways that allow them to interact with more of our multiverse. And this affects the people they interact with as well. It's not that anything followed them home: the bigfoot, dogmen, sprites, and other cryptids were there the whole time.

Chapter 14—Living with Invisible Lifeforms

"You can't depend on your eyes when your imagination is out of focus."—Mark Twain

This book argues that there is another state of matter around us that we don't understand very well. And secret lifeforms use this unique state of matter to access special abilities.

Having read most of this book, you might wonder if I'm out of my mind. I can assure you; I mean every word I've said here. All of the evidence points to invisible lifeforms living around us with associated space-time anomalies, light orbs, and sudden, explained electrical surges. We've talked about it, as a society, a tiny bit in terms of extraterrestrials being here. But we've never had a serious conversation about whether there are other indigenous types of intelligent life all around us that we've never officially acknowledged. We can call them cryptids, but we don't know much about them, just like the multitude of microbes in our bodies and the soil. And those who may formally know about cryptids are not saying much.

And if it's taken me, an open-minded academic, over a half-century to figure this out, it shows how difficult it is to accept and understand. So I get if you're skeptical about the information presented in these chapters, and I suggest you don't take my word for it but do your research and reach your unique conclusions.

Types of Encounters

I've read and listened to hundreds of encounter stories; there seems to be considerable variation in how these encounters play out. In some cases, the bigfoot rescue people from dangerous situations, especially children and the injured. The first time I heard this was from someone at a UFO conference. He told me his aunt had been rescued by something very tall, massive, and hairy after she fell from her horse and was knocked unconscious in California. While she became conscious again, she felt something lift her off the riding path and carry her to a safe location some fifteen feet away. This person told me his aunt could have been trampled by other horses coming that way, so the creature saved her life.

Other cases involve people carried to safety after serious injuries on camping trails, kids rescued after falling in powerful creeks, and kayakers being pulled to safety and fed for a few days by mysterious bipedal creatures. In another alleged case, a massive bipedal creature came out of the woods to lift a car back onto the road after it slipped off (north of Twin Falls, Idaho). And then there are the unexplained stacked rock pyramids, sometimes topped with a forest flower, found around homes and locations of bigfoot sightings.

Bigfoot have also approached people at campsites and shown they needed help in some way, with bodily injuries affecting their infants, for example. In one case in Glacier, a family stayed for two weeks at a campsite after discovering a nearby mother and infant bigfoot needing assistance with a foot injury that they helped heal (both adults, having grown up on farms, had essential veterinary experience skills).[157]

However, there are also many other cases of bigfoot damaging cars, jumping on roofs of moving vehicles, rock-throwing, bluff charges, and all sorts of chaos and mayhem.

In National Parks, there are many cases of rangers or researchers going to remote areas and being followed, intimidated, or chased out, sometimes by bigfoot groups, or simply disappearing altogether.

Bob "Action" Jackson is a former, well-known Yellowstone Park ranger, and he's talked about his bigfoot sightings. Jackson claims to have ridden between 50,000 to 70,000 miles on horseback in Yellowstone's backcountry. As far as I know, he is the only park ranger to come forward so far and talk about his sightings back there. And perhaps it's no coincidence that the Park Service didn't renew his job contract in 2004:

> The first time I heard anything was in the mid-late 70s. An outfitter and I were riding up Fan Creek in the Northwest section of the park. Up the drainage in Stellaria Creek, we heard a sound that just kept going and going. It was probably a mile away. It filled the whole valley up — kind of like 1,000 elk going to their death. I couldn't believe this thing had that much volume for that long a period of time. [My companion] had never heard anything like it, neither.[158]

Trauma and Shock

We don't hear more about these cases because in many cases, the people are severely traumatized, having encountered something they can't describe or didn't believe in. They have Post Traumatic Stress Syndrome. Other times, the creatures harass, howl, or scream at them so seriously and loudly that they are on the brink of losing consciousness. Many witnesses have said it feels like being in front of speakers at a rock concert: you can feel your internal organs vibrating unpleasantly.

A witness near Lake Coeur D'Alene described how loud these Sasquatch screams can be: "I was headed back to camp when I heard a scream so loud it went clear through my body — it was like being at REALLY loud rock concert . . . I dropped to my knees."[159]

So if people are experiencing these encounters but are too shocked, confused or afraid later to talk about it, we won't have a good sense of what's happening. There's a possibility that this general confusion about these encounters serves the interests of the National Park, Forest Services, and other bureaucracies that don't want to take the time to respond to what's going on in these parks.

Where is the Physical Evidence?

You can read about cases of bigfoot bodies recovered in national parks, where good photos are taken, and even giant bones discovered at archeological digs. But in each case I've read about, the witnesses are too shocked by what they saw to share it with anyone else. Park rangers are often told to forget about it or destroy the evidence. "We don't scare people at the green and brown" (Those are the National Park colors).[160] And at other times, local police, and apparent special operations officers accustomed to such encounters, will confiscate phones and tell witnesses to keep quiet "or else."

We're living in a dire situation here. Severe enough for the Pentagon to have had a program directed to study cryptids for several years. I'm not trying to alarm you here, but I suggest that you pay attention to your surroundings when you're out and about.

Be Careful Out There

Maintain complete situation awareness when you're in unfamiliar areas or separated from other people. Cryptids can blend in with their environment or camouflage themselves as tree stumps and boulders. They are also adept at imitating familiar sounds like a human baby crying, pet dogs, you calling for your children, and natural

212 Dark Matter Monsters

animal sounds like owls and coyotes. Interestingly, witnesses say these owl-type sounds are not entirely convincing, nor are other animal imitations. Unsurprisingly, the animal sounds "too big" or "too loud."

One big clue that they're around you is that the whole area suddenly becomes unnaturally quiet. If this happens in your area, pay attention. This strange silence is usually accompanied by feelings of unease that something is off. Your mind might rationalize this to make everything seem OK, but you're better off paying attention and perhaps leaving the area. Don't ignore it. The important thing is to discern whether you perceive a feeling of danger or just surprise and novelty. If you start feeling a deep panic or sudden danger, you should immediately retreat to a place that feels better.

I've never experienced anything remotely like this, either in the woods, plains, or desert. But I know people who have, and it was an indication that something really out of the ordinary was about to happen.

So when you're out there, anywhere beyond your doorway in many places, pay attention and maintain situational awareness. Because you may be the next person to encounter a dark matter monster, and you will likely not see it coming.

Epilogue

As I finished this book, I learned of an excellent new documentary entitled *A Flash of Beauty: Bigfoot Revealed*. It features fantastic photos, fresh thinking, and highly credible witnesses. The analysis at the film's end of why people don't talk about their encounters is spot on, in my view. We have many psychological defense mechanisms for suppressing our memories of meetings with the unknown.

The research of former Soviet scientists V.E. Zhvirblis, N.E. Nevessky, and David Fryberger from Stanford came to light just before I finished writing. It shows that a fractal, Bagel-like magnetic coiled structure called a "SuperTor" (as described in figure 46) produces visible and luminous electronic matter that can persist in the same space even after the electricity is turned off or the device is removed from the table! The authors suggest that this shape lets matter energize directly from the quantum vacuum by slightly altering the relationship between electricity and magnetism, what Fryberger calls "dyality rotation." He believes this creates an object called a "vorton" (yes, think vortex), another type of coherent matter. Their work supports what I've presented in previous chapters, providing an everyday scientific basis for ball lightning, earthlights, and related phenomena.

I also became aware of the work of Travis A. Cisco jr., who found that UFOs can highly magnetize the tops of trees and swirl and twist them around like crop circles in the complete absence of wind. What can temporarily magnetize wood (like the crop circle in Chapter 8)? Theoretically, it's not supposed to happen. Other effects include agitation of animals and cars stalling.

Sound familiar? This research started with the work of UFO researcher Bruce Maccabee who discovered magnetic monopoles around the Gulf Breeze, Florida, sightings in the early 1990s, and other locations with UFO activity like Pine Bush and Long Island, New York. Travis presented his finding on the APEC YouTube channel. It's consistent with the work presented in this book (see Chapter 1) and suggests we're on the right path. When cosmologically interactive, exotic states of matter interact with ordinary matter, weird things happen. Stay tuned for updates at my blog NewCrystalMind.com

Footnotes

1. Lyons, Bigfoot Frightening Encounters, Vol.4, 2019
2. Podcast UFO with Martin Willis, Ep. 486 Dec 21st, 2021
3. Encounters USA, Feb. 4th, 2020. YouTube,
4. Lyons, Bigfoot Frightening Encounters, Vol 4., 2019
5. Paulides, 2017
6. Lockheed Martin Patent SYSTEMS AND METHODS FOR GENERATING COHERENT MATTERWAVE BEAMS US9,502.202B2
7. Winston H. Bostick New York Times article, Dec. 12, 1956
8. Tinsley Interview, 1996
9. SSE Meeting 2015, San Francisco
10. https://en.wikipedia.org/wiki/Simon_Shnoll
11. Leah Broussard, Arxiv, 2017
12. New Scientist, June 5, 2019
13. New Scientist, June 11, 2018
14. Kouropoulos, 2005
15. Lockheed Martin Patent SYSTEMS AND METHODS FOR GENERATING COHERENT MATTERWAVE BEAMS US9,502.202B2
16. Boyd Bushman, Apparatus and method for amplifying a magnetic beam, US5929732
17. Kewanee Lapseritis, International UFO Congress, 2014
18. https://en.wikipedia.org/wiki/Gigantopithecus   CC4.0   License https://creativecommons.org/licenses/by/4.0/
19. Bailey Sasquatch Meeting, Feb . 2022
20. Wootton, 2015
21. Strange Familiars, Ep. 184
22. Wilson, Rocky Mountain Bigfoot Campfire Stories, Chap. 2, 2021
23. May 17, 2022. U.S. House of Representatives, Permanent Select Committee on Intelligence, Subcommittee on Counterterrorism, Counterintelligence, and Counterproliferation,   Washington,   D.C. https://docs.house.gov/meetings/IG/IG05/20220517/114761/HHRG-117-IG05-Transcript-20220517.pdf
24. https://www.nytimes.com/2017/12/16/us/politics/pentagon-program-ufo-harry-reid.html
25. Elliot,   Krissy.   2018.   https://alumni.berkeley.edu/california-magazine/online/so-why-do-people-believe-bigfoot-anyway/
26. Kelleher and Knapp. 2005. Hunt for the Skinwalker
27. Germer, Sasquatch Chronicles, Ep. 697
28. Science,   2020.   "Celebrating   Marie   Tharp." https://www.science.org/doi/10.1126/science.abe7084

29. Wootton, David. 2015.
30. May 12th, 2022. https://thedebrief.org/as-house-panel-prepares-to-examine-unidentified-aerial-phenomena-new-questions-emerge/
31. Lovelace, Terry. 2018
32. https://en.wikipedia.org/wiki/2006_O%27Hare_International_Airport_UFO_sighting
33. https://www.reddit.com/r/UFOs/comments/fcvwjq/pdf_strange_effects_from_ufos_nicap_gordon_lore/
34. Keyhoe and Lore, 1969. P. 61
35. Wheeler, John. 1954. Physical Review
36. Orchard, Vance. 198
37. Hunt for the Skinwalker, 2005
38. Wilson, Yellowstone Bigfoot Campfire Stories, Chap. 7, 2019
39. Germer, Sasquatch Chronicles, Ep. 21
40. Parkhomov and Greenyer.
41. Teordani, 2005
42. Cutchin and Renner, 2020
43. Bailey Conference, May 2021
44. Survivorman Bigfoot, Ep. 10
45. Collected Works, 2021.
46. Wilson, Yellowstone Bigfoot Campfire Stories, Chap. 6, 2019
47. Parkhomov and Greenyer, 2019
48. Facebook comment, April 13, 2022
49. Matsumoto, 2021.
50. Gordon, 2010 and 2022
51. Kelleher and Knapp, 2005.
52. SSE online meeting, Feb. 2022
53. 53.https://www.reddit.com/r/ufo/comments/ozvouk/missing_aatip_slides_leaked_by_christopher_mellon/
54. The Basement Office, YouTube, 2022
55. Joe, private email to author, 2022
56. Lacatski et al., p. 26
57. Arghirescu, 2020
58. Morehead, 2019
59. Lacatski et al., p. 22
60. Matsumoto, Collected Works, p. 42
61. Tinsley Interview, 1996
62. Matsumoto, Collected Works, p. 25
63. Wooton, pp. 144-145, 2005.
64. Matsumoto, Collected Works, p. 31
65. Shoulders, 2006
66. Solin, 1992
67. Matsumoto, 2003
68. Nevessky, 1993
69. Paulides, 2008
70. Ken Shoulder Interview, 2010
71. Martin Fleischmann Memorial Project Channel, YouTube, "Making Galaxies," March 20th, 2022
72. New Scientist, April 1st, 2022
73. YouTube, Sept 16, 2021
74. Bychkov, 1998
75. Bychkov, 2010
76. Ibid.

77. Ibid.
78. AFRL, Ball Lightning Study, 1993
79. AFRL, Eric Davis, Ball Lightning Study, 2003
80. Kouropoulos, 2005; Fryberger, 1994 & 2009
81. Singer, 1972
82. Fryberger, p. 18, 1994
83. Matsumoto, Collected Writings, 2021
84. Morehead, 2017
85. McCullough, 2015
86. Wootton, 2015
87. Phillips, 2009 presentation
88. Cutchin and Renner, p. 33, 2020
89. Shoulders, 2006
90. Kouropoulos, 2005
91. Stakhanov, 1979
92. Bychkov, p. 238, 2010
93. Chernobrov, 2003
94. Bychkov, 2010
95. Collins, 1992
96. Hein, 2013
97. Scott, Spaced Out Radio, Jan 14th, 2022
98. Germer, Sasquatch Chronicles, Ep. 497
99. Jackson interview, 2003
100. Chaitin, p. 15, 2006
101. Martin Willis Podcast, #501, April 5th, 2022
102. Cutchin and Renner. Vol. 1, 2020
103. Bailey Conference, 2021
104. Germer, Sasquatch Chronicles, Ep. 841
105. Germer, Sasquatch Chronicles, Aug. 27th, Ep. 786
106. Strange Familiars, Ep. 184
107. Hunt, 2021
108. Twitter, March 23nd, 2022
109. Wilson, Yellowstone Bigfoot Campfire Stories, Chap. 1, 2019
110. Germer, Sasquatch Chronicles, Ep. 841
111. Wilson, Yellowstone Bigfoot Campfire Stories, Chap. 7, 2019
112. Wilson, Montana Bigfoot Campfire Stories, Chap. 5, 2020
113. Buschardt, 2021
114. http://www.bigfootencounters.com/classics/beck.htm
115. Paulides, p. 10, 2008
116. Lyons, Bigfoot Frightening Encounters, Vol 12, Report #2, 2020
117. Buschardt, p. 73, 2021
118. Buckner, p. 68, 2014
119. Parkhomov, 2019
120. Parkhomov, p. 89, 2019
121. Myers, 2021
122. Gordon, p. 146, 1973
123. Cutchkin and Renner, pp. 245-6, 2020.
124. Sasquatch Chronicles, Ep. 497
125. Lyons, Bigfoot Frightening Encounters, Vol 1, Report #1, 2018
126. Sasquatch Chronicles, Ep. 515
127. Sasquatch Chronicles, Ep. 533
128. Lyons, Bigfoot Frightening Encounters, 2020
129. Lyons, Bigfoot Frightening Encounters, p. 10, 2019

130. Wilson, Yellowstone Bigfoot Campfire Stories, Chap. 7, 2019
131. Sasquatch Chronicles, Ep. 697
132. Buschardt, p. 158, 2021
133. Buschardt, p. 142, 2021
134. Spaced Out Radio, Jan. 27, 2022
135. Lapseritis, International UFO Congress, 2014
136. Cutchin and Renner, 2020
137. David Paulides, April 20th, 2022 https://youtu.be/UWTksB-uUvY
138. Cutchin and Renner, Vol. 2, 2020
139. Buschardt, p. 131, 2021
140. Wilson, Yellowstone Bigfoot Campfire Stories, Chap. 2019
141. Bailey Bigfoot Conference, 2021
142. Tiller et al., 2005
143. Martin Fleischmann Memorial Project, YouTube
144. Zhvirblis, 1995.
145. Matsumoto, Collected Works, Mechanisms of Cold Fusion, p. 221
146. Roth, 1993
147. https://cerncourier.com/a/relic-neutrinos-a-challenge-for-the-next-millennium/
148. New Scientist, Nov. 8th, 2021
149. https://archive.org/details/PhysicalReviewX
150. New Scientist, Nov. 5th, 2014
151. Ibid.
152. Shoulders, 2006
153. The Black Vault, YouTube, Feb. 4th, 2022
154. Shoulders, 2006
155. Edge Science, No. 50, 2022
156. Collins, 1992
157. Wilson, Glacier Bigfoot Campfire Stories, Chap. 9, 2020
158. Bob Jackson Interview with T.E. Stein, 2003
159. Cook, p. 29, 2019
160. Wilson, Yellowstone Bigfoot Campfire Stories, Chap.9, 2019
161. Lyons, Bigfoot Frightening Encounters, Vol. 12, 2021

Bibliography

Afafune and Takeda. 2002. "Total Reflection of Relic Neutrinos on Material Targets." Institute for Cosmic Ray Research, University of Tokyo, https://www.icepp.s.u-tokyo.ac.jp/papers/ps/icepp-report/ut-icepp-08-02.pdf

Arghirescu, Marius. 2020. "Two explanatory hypotheses for the generation of lightning and ball-lightning phenomena." *Physics and Astronomy International Journal*. Vol 4, Issue. 4 *https://www.researchgate.net/publication/348934743_Two_explanatory_hypotheses_for_the_generation_of_lightning_and_ball-lightning_phenomena*

Beck, Fred.1967. "I FOUGHT THE APEMEN OF MOUNT ST. HELENS, WA. *http://www.bigfootencounters.com/classics/beck.htm*

Bockris, John O'Meara, 2013. *The New Paradigm: A Confrontation Between Physics and the Paranormal Phenomena.* New Energy Foundation.

Bostick, Winston H. 1958. "Possible Hydromagnetic Simulation of Cosmical Phenomena in the Laboratory" Cosmical Gas Dynamics, Proceedings from IAU Symposium no. 8. Edited by Johannes Martinus Burgers and Richard Nelson Thomas. International Astronomical Union. Symposium no. 8, p. 1090
———, V. Nardi, J. Feugeas, and W. Prior. 1980. "Internal Structure of Beam Filaments." *Physical Review A.* https://doi.org/10.1103/PhysRevA.22.2211

Brooks, Michael. June 5th, 2019. "We've seen signs of a mirror-image universe that is touching our own" *NewScientist*

Buckner, Paul G. Bigfoot, UFO's & The Paranormal: True Encounters. Last Wednesday Writers, LLC. Kindle Edition.

Buschardt, Carter, 2021. *Bigfoot: Evidence of an Enigma* (Second Edition). Kindle Edition.
———. *Spaced Out Radio*. YouTube. January 27th, 2022. Accessed: June 1st, 2022

Burtsev, Igor. May 2021. Bailey, CO Bigfoot Conference: Russia and USA.
———. April 13, 2022. Facebook comment, personal profile page.

Bychkov, VL, Gennady V. Golubkov, and Anatoly I. Nikitin, ed.. 2010. *The Atmosphere and the Ionosphere:Dymamics, Processes and Monitoring.* Springer: Berlin.

———. 2012. "Unsolved Mystery of Ball Lightning." Available from: *https://www.researchgate.net/publication/258725130_Unsolved_Mystery_of_Ball_Lightning*

Byrne, Peter. 2013. *The Many Lives of Hugh Everett III.* Oxford University Press; Reprint edition

Carroll, Sean. 2019. *Something Deeply Hidden: Quantum Worlds and the Emergence of Spacetime.* Dutton

Cameron, David. 2007. The Harvard Gazette. https://news.harvard.edu/gazette/story/2007/07/obesity-is-contagious/

Chaitin, Gregory. 2006. *MetaMath: The Search for Omega.* Vintage

Chown, Marcus. 2000, June 16th. "Shadow Worlds." New Scientist.

Concavenator. 2017. Drawing of Gigantopicthecus. Creative Commons 4.0 https://creativecommons.org/licenses/by-sa/4.0/deed.ens

Collins, Andrew. 1992. *The New Circlemakers.* 4th Dimension Press. Virginia Beach, VA.

Collins, Kenny. 2021. Bailey Conference: Russia and America, May 2021. Bailey Lodge.

Cook, Becky. 2015. *Bigfoot Still Lives in Idaho.* Kindle edition.

Cutchin, Joshua and Timothy Renner. 2020. *Where the Footprints End: High Strangeness and the Bigfoot Phenomenon. Volume 1 Folklore.* Dark holler Arts
———. 2020. *Where the Footprints End:High Strangeness and the Bigfoot Phenomenon.Volume 2 Evidence.* Dark holler Arts

Davis. Eric W. 2003. "Ball Lightning Study." AFRL-PR-ED-TR-2002-0039

Dennett, Preston E.. 2017. *Inside UFOs: True Accounts of Contact with Extraterrestrials.* Blue Giant Books

Delonge, Tom. 2022. March 23rd, Twitter.

Egley, George. 1989. "Hungarian Ball Lightning" in *The Science of Ball Lightning*. International Symposium on the Science of Ball Lightning (FIRE BALL), Tokyo, Japan, https://doi.org/10.1142/0707
————. 2016. "Transmutation by Dust Fusion." Issue 130. November/December. Infinite Energy Magazine.

Elliot, Krissy. 2018. Cal Alumni Assc. *California Magazine*. https://alumni.berkeley.edu/california-magazine/online/so-why-do-people-believe-bigfoot-anyway/

Forward, Robert L., 1963. "Guidelines to Antigravity." American Journal of Physics, Vol. 31, No. 3, 166-170.

Fryberger, David. 1994. "A Model for Ball Lighting," Stanford Linear Accelerator Center, SLAC-PUB-6473
————. 2009. "A Ball Lightning Model as a Possible Explanation of Recently Reported Cavity Lights," Stanford Linear Accelerator Center, SLAC-PUB-13583

Germer, Wes. (Dec. 8th). Sasquatch Chronicles Radio // SC EP: 497 "Do Not Pull Over." Retrieved January 25, 2022 from *https://sasquatchchronicles.com/*
————. (Feb.15th). Sasquatch Chronicles Radio // SC EP: 515 "I Shouldn't Be Alive." Retrieved January 25, 2022 from *https://sasquatchchronicles.com/*
————. (April 14th). Sasquatch Chronicles Radio // SC EP: 533 "Chanting in the Woods." Retrieved January 25, 2022 from *https://sasquatchchronicles.com/*
————. (Dec. 20th). Sasquatch Chronicles Radio // SC EP: 610 "Encounters with the Strange." Retrieved January 25, 2022 from *https://sasquatchchronicles.com/*
————. (Dec.13th, 2021). Sasquatch Chronicles Radio // SC EP: 697 "Whirlwind of Weirdness." Retrieved January 25, 2022 from https://sasquatchchronicles.com/
————. (Nov.13th, 2021). Sasquatch Chronicles Radio // SC EP: 715 "These Monsters Chasing Me." Retrieved January 25, 2022 from *https://sasquatchchronicles.com/*
————. (Aug 27th). Sasquatch Chronicles Radio // SC EP: 786 "My Father Shot It in the Front Yard." Retrieved January 25, 2022 from *https://sasquatchchronicles.com/*
————. (April 1st). Sasquatch Chronicles Radio // SC EP: 841 "We Are Moving." Retrieved June 20, 2022 from *https://sasquatchchronicles.com/*

Gibney, E. "Quantum Cloud Simulates Magnetic Monopole." Nature (2014). *https://doi.org/10.1038/nature.2014.14612*

Gordon, Stan.. 2010. Silent Invasion: The Pennsylvania UFO-Bigfoot Casebook.
————. 2022. Martin Willis Podcast UFO. Ep. #501 April 5th,

Greenstreet, Stephen. 2022. "UFOs, Werewolves & Ghosts | Shocking truth of Pentagon AAWSAP program" May 12th. The Basement Office. *https://youtu.be/6XD4gQS_-qY*

Greenyer, Robert William. Nov. 21st, 2021."Matsumoto - Steps to the Discovery of Electro-Nuclear Collapse " Martin Fleischmann Memorial Project YouTube Channel. *https://youtu.be/Ur1d07OrWOQ*
————. Aug. 17th, 2021."Technological production of 'Ball Lightning' vs natural formation" Martin Fleischmann Memorial Project YouTube Channel.
————. Dec. 19th, 2021."Make and Break." Martin Fleischmann Memorial Project YouTube Channel. *https://youtu.be/cc_k6dskp5g*
————. Jan 23rd, 2022."Reconstitution—End of the EVO" Martin Fleischmann Memorial Project YouTube Channel.
————. April 24th, 2022. "Hutchison Effect - The sword in the stone" Martin Fleischmann Memorial Project YouTube Channel. *https://youtu.be/9F7MFpZ0OUU*

Hein, Simeon. 2002. *Opening Minds: A Journey of Extraordinary Encounters, Crop Circles, and Resonance.* Mount Baldy Press, inc.: Boulder, CO
————. 2017 *Black Swan Ghosts: A Sociologist Encounters Witnesses to Unexplained Aerial Craft, Their Occupants And Other Elements of the Multiverse.* Mount Baldy Press, inc.: Boulder, CO

————. 2007. Presentation to Society for Scientific Exploration. "Crop Circles" East Lansing, Michigan.

————. 2013. "Investigation into Dark Energy as the Cause of Anomalous Electromagnetic Activity Observed in the Vicinity of Crop Formations." Unpublished abstract, Research Gate. *https://www.researchgate.net/publication/240213863_Investigation_into_Dark_Energy_as_the_Cause_of_Anomalous_Electromagnetic_Activity_Observed_in_the_Vicinity_of_Crop_Formations*

Heine, Matthew. Feb. 4th, 2020. "Crop Circle Expert & Remote Viewing Sociologist Author Simeon Hein" Encounters USA // Retrieved January 25, 2022 from https://YouTube.com

Israel, Ruckhaber et al. 1931 *One Hundred Authors Against Einstein.*

Jackson, Bob. 2003. Interview. *http://squatchable.com/article.asp?id=680*

Keel, John. 1975. *The Mothman Prophecies.* Saturday Review Press.

Kelleher, Colm A. and Knapp, George. 2005. *Hunt for the Skinwalker: Science Confronts the Unexplained at a Remote Ranch in Utah.* Pocket Books.

Keyhoe, Donald and Gordon Lore, 1969. "Strange Effects of UFOs." NICAP

King, P.D. 2020. *Dogman, Bigfoot, and Something More, Volume 1: A Brief Collection of Encounters.* Kindle Ed.

Kouropoulos, C.P., 2005. "Classically Bound Electrons—EVs, Exotic Chemistry & 'Cold Electricity'"
———. "Self-Magnetized Electronic Filaments"
https://arxiv.org/pdf/physics/0506124.pdf

Lacatski, James T., Kelleher, Colm and George Knapp. 2021. *Skinwalkers at the Pentagon: An Insiders' Account of the Secret Government UFO Program.* RTMA, LLC. Kindle Edition.

Lapseritis, Kiwanee, 2011. *The Sasquatch People and their Interdimensional Connection.* Commanche Spirit Publishing.

———. 2014. International UFO Congress. Fountain Hills, AZ

Leonov, R.A. 1965. "Ball Lightning Enigma." USSR

Lozneanu, Erzilia et al. 2007. "Ball Lightning as Self-Organized Complexity." *https://www.researchgate.net/publication/1762350_Ball_Lightning_as_a_Self-Organized_Complexity*

Lyons, Tom. 2018. *Bigfoot Frightening Encounters, Volume 1*, Kindle Ed.
———. 2019. *Bigfoot Frightening Encounters, Volume 2*, Kindle Ed.
———. 2019. *Bigfoot Frightening Encounters, Volume 3*, Kindle Ed.
———. 2019. *Bigfoot Frightening Encounters, Volume 4*, Kindle Ed.
———. 2019. *Bigfoot Frightening Encounters, Volume 6*, Kindle Ed.
———. 2020. *Bigfoot Frightening Encounters: Volume 12*, Kindle Ed.

Lovelace, Terry. 2018. *Incident at Devil's Den: A True Story.* Kindle Ed.
———. 2020. *Devil's Den: The Reckoning.* Kindle Ed.

Matsumoto, Takaaki. 2019. "Nattoh Model for Cold Fusion". United States: Web.
———. EGS - AGU - EUG Joint Assembly, Abstracts from the meeting held in Nice, France, 6 - 11 April 2003, abstract id. 13998
———. 2021. *Steps to the Discovery of Electro-Nuclear Collapse: Collected Papers (1989–1999)*, Translated by Robert William Greenyer.

McCullough, David. 2015. *The Wright Brothers.* Simon and Schuster. New York

McFeely, Harriett. 2021. *A Walk on the Weird Side in Nebraska*. Bigfoot Crossroads. Hastings, NE

Mellon, Chris. 2022. "Is the Air Force Hiding Something?" *TheDebrief.org* Feb. 3rd.

Mesyats. G., 1997. Ectons and their Role in Electrical Discharges in Vacuum and Gases. Journal de Physique IV Proceedings, EDP Sciences, 1997, 07 (C4), pp.C4-93-C4-112. 10.1051/jp4:1997407 .
jpa-00255563

—————. 1996. "Ecton processes at the cathode in a vacuum discharge," Proceedings of the XVIIth International Symposium on Discharges and Electrical Insulation in Vacuum, Berkeley, CA, pp. 721-731, July 21-26.

Myers, Jim. 2021. "Intelligence and Consciousness of Bigfoot/Sasquatch" Zoom Presentation to Boulder EXO group. Boulder, Colorado.

Monroe, Donald L. 2013. *The Braided Horse Are Coming*. Spatial Systems Publishing. Billings, MT

Morehead, Ronald and Powell, Thomas. 2012. *Voices in the Wilderness: A True Story*. Sierra Sounds: Mariposa, CA

Morehead, Ronald. 2017. *The Quantum Bigfoot*. Sierra Sounds: Mariposa, CA

Mungia, Lance. 2019. *Third Eye Spies*. https://www.imdb.com/title/tt5112424/

Nevessky, N.E. 1993. "Electromagnetic Fields of Current Structures." Electricity Journal.

O'Neill, Ian. 2019. *History.com* "Black Holes Were Such an Extreme Concept, Even Einstein Had His Doubts". April 15, 2019

Orchard, Vance. 1993. *Bigfoot of the Blues*. Walla Walla, WA

Parkhomov, Alexander. 2019. *Space.Earth. Human.*: New Views on Science. Translated by Robert William Greenyer

Paulides, David. 2008. *The Hoopa Project: Bigfoot Encounters in California*. Handcock House Publishers, Blaine, WA.
—————. 2009. *Tribal Bigfoot. Handcock House Publishers*, Blaine, WA.

Phillips, Ted. 2009. Presentation to Arkansas UFO Conference.

Renner, Timothy. Aug. 6th, 2020. "It Moved Like a Spider." *Strange Familiars*, Ep. 184 https://Youtube.com. Accessed Jun 25, 2022

Romano, Marco and Francesco Latino Chiocci. Dec. 18, 2020. "Celebrating Marie Tharp." *Science*. Vol. 370, Issue 6523, pp. 1415-16

Rosencrantz, Daniel J.,.2021. "Fundamental limitations on efficiently forecasting certain epidemic measures in network models*" Computer Sciences and Integrative Biology,* https://www.pnas.org/doi/10.1073/pnas.2109228119

Roth, J. Reece. 1993. "Ball lightning: What nature is trying to tell the plasma research community" International Conference on Plasma Sciences (ICOPS), 1993, pp. 109-, doi: 10.1109/PLASMA.1993.593116.

Shoulders, Ken. 1987. EV: A Tale of Discovery. Jupiter Technologies.
————. 2007. "Teleportation using EVO's." Collected Works.
————. 2006. "Dark Matter Messengers." Collected Works.
————. 2007. "Electron Ensembles." Collected Works.
————. 2007. "The Good, the Bad, and the Ugly." Collected Works.
————. 2010. "Interview with John Hutchison."

Singer, Stanley, 1971. *The Nature of Ball Lightning*. Springer
————. (2002). *Ball Lightning-The Scientific Effort*. Philosophical Transactions: Mathematical, Physical and Engineering Sciences, 360(1790), 5–9.
http://www.jstor.org/stable/3066601

Slezak, Michael. Nov. 5th, 2014. "Ghost universes kill Schrödinger's quantum cat" *NewScientist* https://www.newscientist.com/article/mg22429944-000-ghost-universes-kill-schrodingers-quantum-cat/

Stakhanov, I.P. 1979. *Ball Lightening's Physical Nature*, Moscow: Atomizdat

Stenhoff, M. 1976. "Ball Lightning." Nature 260, 596 (1976)
————2006. Ball Lightning: An Unsolved Problem in Atmospheric Physics, Springer Science and Business Media

Spergel, David N. 2015. "The dark side of cosmology: Dark matter and dark energy." *Science*. Vol 347 Issue 6226

Stroud, Les. Survivorman Bigfoot. Sept. 4th, 2020. "Portland Oregon," Ep. 10. YouTube.com. *https://youtu.be/N-ILD09_iK0*

Taleb, Nassim Nicholas. 2010. *The Black Swan: Second Edition: The Impact of the Highly Improbable*. Random House Publishing Group; 2nd ed. edition (May 11, 2010)

Tegmark, Max. 2014. *Our Mathematical Universe: My Quest for the Ultimate Nature of Reality*. Vintage

Teordarani, M. 2004. "A Long-Term Scientific Survey of the Hessdalen Phenomenon". *Journal of Scientific Exploration.*

Tiller, William A., Walter E. Dibble, Jr., and J. Gregory Fandel. 2005. *Some Adventures With Real Magic*. Pavior Publishing: Walnut Creek, CA

Tinsley, Christopher P. 1996. "Interview with Martin Fleischmann." *Infinite Energy Magazine.*

ThinkerThunker. 2021. *How to Find and Film Bigfoot: An Exercise in Critical Thinking*. Kindle Ed. *ThinkerThunker.com*

Tonomura, A, et al. 1986. "Evidence for Aharonov-Bohm Effect with Magnetic Field Completely Shielded from Electron Wave." *Physical Review Letters*, 56, 792-795. https://doi.org/10.1103/PhysRevLett.56.792

Westrum, Ron. (May 3rd, 2019). Society for Scientific Exploration // "Hidden Events: Portal Areas." Retrieved January 30, 2022 from https://YouTube.com/

Wheeler, John. 1955. "Geons." Physical Review. Vol. 97 No. 2.

Wilson, Rusty. 2019. *Rusty Wilson's Yellowstone Bigfoot Campfire Stories* . Yellow Cat Publishing.
————. 2020. *Rusty Wilson's Glacier Bigfoot Campfire Stories* . Yellow Cat Publishing.
————. 2020. *Rusty Wilson's Rocky Mountain Bigfoot Campfire Stories* . Yellow Cat Publishing.
————. *Rusty Wilson's Montana Bigfoot Campfire Stories* . Yellow Cat Publishing.

Wooton, David. 2015. The Invention of Science: A New History of the Scientific Revolution. HarperCollins Publishers.

Travis,Tritten. 2022. "How Believers in the Paranormal Birthed the Pentagon's New Hunt for UFOs" *military.com* *https://www.military.com/daily-news/2022/03/07/how-believers-paranormal-birthed-pentagons-new-hunt-ufos.html*

Tonomura, Akira. 1986."Evidence for Aharonov-Bohm Effect by Electron Holography" *Physical Review Letters* 99, 210401

UFO Podcast with Martin Willis, Ep. 501, April 5th, 2022
————. Ep. 486, Dec. 21st, 2021

Urutskeov, LI. Liksonov V.I. "Observation of transformation of chemical elements during electric discharge" "RECOM" RRC "Kurchatov Institute" Moscow, Shchukinskaya

Zhvirblis, VE. 1995. "The Bagel Game." *Electricity Magazine*. Translated by Robert William Greenyer.

Index

About the Author

Dr. Simeon Hein is the director of the Mount Baldy Institute, a research and teaching company, which he founded in 1997, to give people the opportunity to learn Resonant Viewing, a type of intuition training that taps into our creative unconscious intelligence. He also studies crop circles and leads crop circle tours in the UK. He is an avid acoustic guitarist: listen at OpeningMindsMusic.com. His previous books include *Opening Minds: A Journey of Extraordinary Encounters, Crop Circles, and Resonance* and *Black Swan Ghosts: A sociologist encounters witnesses to unidentified aerial craft, their occupants, and other elements of the multiverse.* You can find Simeon on YouTube and Twitter. His blog is NewCrystalMind.com.

For More Information
Please Visit DarkMatterMonsters.com

Books by Simeon Hein

BlackSwanGhosts.com

OpeningMinds.info

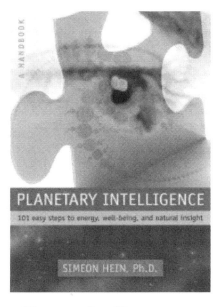

PlanetaryIntelligence.com

Printed in Great Britain
by Amazon

14365147R00133